Mosaic of New Mexico's Scenery,
Rocks, and History

COVER: Redondo Peak, from Jemez Canyon
(Forest Service, U.S.D.A., by John Whiteside)

(*Forest Service, U.S.D.A., by Robert W. Talbott*)

WHITEWATER CANYON NEAR GLENWOOD

SCENIC TRIPS TO THE GEOLOGIC PAST

NO. 8

Mosaic of New Mexico's Scenery, Rocks, and History

edited by

PAIGE W. CHRISTIANSEN

and

FRANK E. KOTTLOWSKI

NEW MEXICO BUREAU OF MINES AND MINERAL RESOURCES

1972

Third edition, 5th printing

Published by Authority of State of New Mexico, NMSA 1953 Sec. 63-1-4
Printed by University of New Mexico Printing Plant, Albuquerque, June 1988

Available from New Mexico Bureau of Mines & Mineral Resources, Socorro, NM 87801

Contents

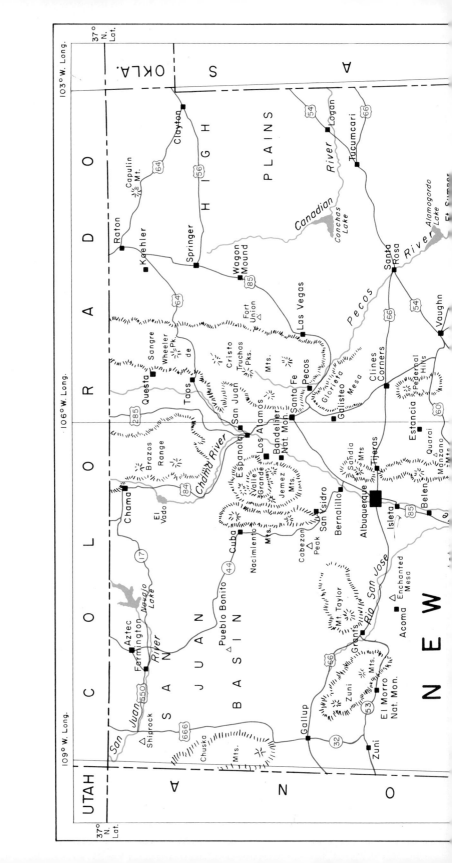

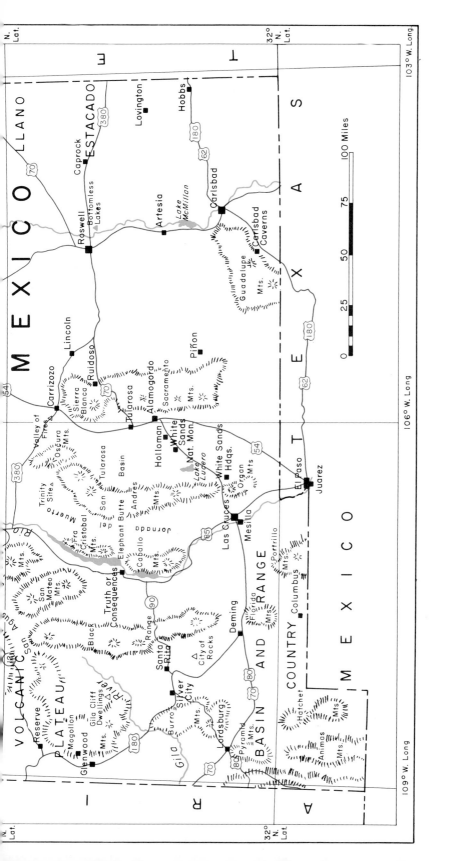

Preface

Previous *Scenic Trips to the Geologic Past* have emphasized scenic tours of local areas in New Mexico. This book lays out a mosaic of facts and fancies concerning the state's landscapes, the rocks that underlie and make up the landscapes, and the history of the people now living or who have lived amid New Mexico's exciting and varied scenery. We hope these short articles will help you enjoy our state, whether you are a tourist driving through at seventy miles an hour, a visitor with a little time to explore, or an old-timer who remembers the cattle drives.

The idea for this publication grew out of a booklet, *New Mexico Mosaic of Science and History*, that was written for the 1963 National Science Fair-International held in Albuquerque. The National Science Fair booklet was directed specifically to the Fair participants and emphasized their tours to famous scientific installations in New Mexico, areas of scenic geologic wonders, and points of historic and archeologic importance. The booklet had only limited distribution; subsequent interest in this kind of publication about New Mexico led to the preparation of this book.

Scenic Trips No. 8 is in two major parts. First, there are articles of general statewide interest to acquaint visitor and resident alike with the Land of Enchantment—its history, flora and fauna, geology, and scenic beauty. Second, there are articles describing specific scenic, geologic, historic, and recreational places to give a depth of understanding and a more intimate view of New Mexico. The entire mosaic of New Mexico thus presented is a permanent record to recall vistas of New Mexico's enchanting land and fascinating history.

ACKNOWLEDGMENTS

Many people have contributed their time and talents to this co-operative undertaking. We thank each of the authors of the articles; where their affiliation is not given, they are staff members of the New Mexico Bureau of Mines and Mineral Resources division of the New Mexico Institute of Mining and Technology. Professor Christiansen is a member of the Humanities Department of the Institute's College division. This book would have been incomplete without the co-operation of the New Mexico Department of Game and Fish, the Museum of New Mexico, the New Mexico Department of Development, the State Park Commission, the U.S. Park Service, and the Forest Service, Southwestern Region, U.S. Department of Agriculture. Our special appreciation goes to Dr. Ross Calvin for his interpretative description of New Mexico's unique flora.

Black and white photographs were contributed by Robert Bieberman, Roy Foster, and Teri Ray of the Bureau of Mines staff and by the authors

1

or their agencies. Some of the drawings were made by David H. Money-penny. Acknowledgment is also made to Mr. Elliott S. Barker and the Forest Service for their willing loan of color transparencies.

Among the numerous personnel of the New Mexico Institute of Mining and Technology who aided in preparation of this book, appreciation is due Helen Waxler, Lois Devlin, Lola White, Mary Ann Grandjean, and Sharon Ballenger for typing of manuscripts and William Arnold, Robert Price, and Raymond Molina for drafting maps and figures. Teri Ray deserves special mention for her interest and editorial advice and for nursing the material from rough manuscripts into printed pages.

PREFACE TO SECOND EDITION

The kind reception given our attempt to provide a brief but comprehensive guide to New Mexico's scenery, rocks, and history resulted in distribution of 5000 copies in two years, and led to this second edition. In this revision, we have incorporated changes that have occurred during these two years, especially the addition of State Parks, and Teri Ray has added an index to make the book more usable. Each author has re-edited his article and made changes where necessary. William Arnold added much material to the index map; typing of the revision manuscript was carefully done by Lois Devlin. Alfred Coulloudon and Wayne Bera supplied additional photographs. Teri Ray initiated revision of the first edition, worked with authors, and guided the manuscript from the authors to the final copy.

PREFACE TO THIRD EDITION

The first edition appeared in 1964, the second in 1967, and a reprint in 1968. In the present edition front matter has been re-styled, printed matter has been altered on the inside and outside of the covers, a footnote added to page 104, and a less bulky paper used.

Of Indians, Spaniards, and Americans

by PAIGE W. CHRISTIANSEN

In the world of the twentieth century with its tumultuous ovation for each discovery of science, with its language of non-Euclidian space, with new heroes who leave the earth, not discover it—sometimes it is refreshing to look back on other days, to see other heroes, and to seek romance and excitement which was equally spectacular in times past. Yet there is a close affinity and a spiritual link among the heroes of the past, the present, and the future, and the reaction of their contemporaries to their feats of glory is not so different. Heroes are those who seek the unknown, who risk life and position to expand the frontiers of man's universe and mind. But heroes can only lead an age, never surpass it. History, then, is people and their catalyst, ideas.

The history of New Mexico, like twentieth century science, is multi-dimensional. Its complex cultural patterns fit with the intricate variety of its geologic wonders and its flora and fauna. In reality, New Mexico is a part of a broader concept, the Southwest. This vast region, which includes western Texas, New Mexico, Arizona, southern California, part of southern Colorado, and southern Utah, has given rise to some of man's greatest achievements. Here prehistoric man rose above his animal heritage to take control of these lands. Here, also, many millennia later, man achieved one of his greatest scientific wonders, the successful release of atomic energy. The story of the years between these events, so far separated in time, is a wondrous tale.

INDIAN BEGINNINGS

Before the coming of the white man, this land belonged to nature's children, the Indian. Centuries before European nations came into existence, peoples from Asia, crossing by the Bering waters, had discovered, explored, and settled the American continents from Alaska to Tierra del Fuego. They mastered the plains, the northern forests, the jungles of Central and South America, and the arid regions. In the deserts and mountains of the Southwest, they conquered elements and terrain, first to survive and then slowly to ascend the ladder of culture.

At first they were foragers, living on what nature provided. At the time of Christ, several groups could be distinguished: In the Colorado River drainage, south of the Grand Canyon, were the Yuman Foragers; in southeastern Arizona and southwestern New Mexico were the Mogollon people; in the Four Corners area (where the states of Utah, Colorado, Arizona, and New Mexico meet) and in the Rio Grande Valley of New

3

Mexico was a complex of cave sites that evidenced a forager type of culture. But, as man always aspires to rise above his environment, the Indian slowly and painfully learned to make tools, developed new techniques, and finally made the great step upward; he domesticated plants. Agriculture, based primarily on the growing of corn, came to the Four Corners before the Christian era. Gradually, out of the primitive foragers, there developed across the Southwest a complex pattern of agricultural societies; peaceful farmers intent upon harvesting the utmost from a harsh land. In Arizona, the Hohokam peoples created a culture based upon irrigation. In the valleys of the upper Gila and Mimbres rivers of southwestern New Mexico, several branches of the Mogollon culture grew and prospered. In the Four Corners area and in the upper Rio Grande Valley, the Mesa Verde, the Gran Chaco, and later the Rio Grande branches developed, at first in the cliffs of the high country, then in open villages along the main tributaries of the Rio Grande. That there were numerous and varied cultures is attested to by the ruins one finds scattered throughout the Southwest. Along now dry arroyos, on buttes overlooking rivers or dry river beds, among cliffs in the mountain fastnesses and in caves wherever they appear, there are thousands of sites whose people and history are lost in antiquity.

And these people were builders. They lived in caves at first, then in crude pit houses. Finally they moved above the ground and evolved building techniques and styles of architecture that stood the ravages of time and still serve the people of the Southwest. In the city of Santa Fe, the Palace of the Governors was built upon the ruins of an Indian pueblo (village), the name of which has disappeared even from tradition, and its massive walls of puddled adobe, laid down before the art of making bricks

PREHISTORIC INDIAN CLIFF DWELLING

4

was introduced by the Spanish, may be seen under glass in some of the rooms of the Palace at the present time. Perhaps most spectacular are the great houses of Chaco Canyon, some of which must have sheltered from one to two thousand people each, and which as achievements in building, both from the standpoint of durability and graceful construction, rival the structures of the historic valleys and plateaus of the ancient eastern world.

In addition to agriculture and building, the Indian of the Southwest achieved great heights in artistic forms. The ceramics of the American Southwest become increasingly important when compared with products of the Old World. The Indians of America and the Southwest are a race of artists. Their aesthetic culture towers above anything achieved by the white man, with the general exception of ancient Greece and Renaissance Italy.

As impressive as his achievements in domesticating plants, in building massive structures, and in developing symbolism and aesthetic values to match his material advances, the Indian's greatest heights were reached in his philosophy on nature and life. He conceived himself to be, not master of creation, but a single factor in the scheme of things. He shared with all things—beasts, birds, rocks, trees, everything in nature—a life principle which permeated all, a gift conferred by the mighty powers of earth and sky. He observed orderly procession of natural phenomena and ordered his own life in harmony therewith. His was no egocentric point of view which has become so much a part of the philosophic base of the European mentality. His natural philosophy entered into every facet of his life—his daily work, his art, his ceramics, his religion. In short, this singularly fine outlook upon the world helps to account for his success in conquering the diverse elements of earth and sky which constantly threatened his very existence.

But this fine culture did not survive in the fullness of its bloom. What eventually destroyed the vast and complicated agricultural system was not the rigors of Mother Nature but a migration of new people into the flow of Southwest history. Sometime after 1000 A.D., a nonfarming, nomadic, warlike people entered the Southwest. The peaceful farmers, weakened by drouth, were unable to cope with this new force. Gradually they fell back, leaving behind their homes, their fields, their culture. By 1300, only a small remnant remained, that located in the Rio Grande Valley of north-central New Mexico. Across the rest of the Southwest the nomadic tribes, technically called *Athapascan* from their linguistic affiliation but better known by their modern name, *Apache,* had replaced the farming cultures. The picturesque Indian pueblos we see today in the valleys of northern New Mexico are the direct descendants of the great cultures that existed at Mesa Verde, Gran Chaco, Frijoles, and other centers of cultural achievement.

The Indians of the Rio Grande Valley and the Apache who controlled most of the Southwest managed an uneasy coexistence. The Pueblo Indians remained basically farmers, holding fast to the cultural advances made by their ancestors during the millennium preceding 1300. The

5

Apache, for the most part, remained nomadic predators, living off nature's bounty, or better still, raiding the pueblos for food. The Apache groups began to take on names and traditional areas which they called their own. In northern New Mexico were the Jicarilla Apache and in the southeast, the Lipan, the Mescalero, and the Natage Apache. In northeastern Arizona were the Navajo and in the drainage of the Gila River, the Chiricahua, the Gila, and other groups of the Western Apache. Each of these groups made its mark upon the face of the land.

SPANISH CONTRIBUTIONS

This was the situation in the Southwest when the sixteenth century opened, but a new force was abroad which would grow and strengthen and leave a deep imprint on New Mexico. Beginning on the wild islands of the Caribbean and then fanning out into the heart of Mexico and the South American continent, this new force spread across the face of America. Europeans, more exactly, Spaniards, came bent upon conquest for its own reward, for the glory of God, and for gold. These sturdy men from the Iberian peninsula with weapons vastly superior to the Indians', with the horse which made them highly mobile and devastating in battle, and with tactics and precision in warfare unknown among the Indians, were to sweep without serious setback across the great cultures of Mexico and Central and South America. By 1540, they were ready to take their next leap forward.

On the west coast of Mexico, at a place called Culiacan, a colorful host gathered. In their ears rang the words of the legend of the Seven Cities of Cibola, seven golden cities, a legend which had been popular in Spain for many generations. Mexico City had produced wealth, and the Spanish were ready to believe that other fabulous cities existed. One Spaniard had already crossed part of North America and had heard from the Indians tales of the rich cities. His name was Cabeza de Vaca, and the exuberance of his tales fired the imagination of the Spaniards.

The soldiers and adventurers gathering in Mexico, commanded by Francisco Vasquez de Coronado, were the first Europeans to organize an expedition to the American Southwest. Leaving from Culiacan in 1540, they went up the west coast of Mexico into modern Arizona, then east into New Mexico. The seven golden cities turned out to be the pueblos around Zuni, New Mexico, and not golden at all. The expedition, although discouraged, marched into the Rio Grande Valley and visited most of the pueblos there. Still they failed to find the treasure they sought. In a final desperate attempt, they explored onto the Great Plains, eventually reaching central Kansas. Broken in spirit and body, they struggled back to the Rio Grande Valley, and then retraced their route to Mexico. In all, the expedition covered a two-year span. A failure? Yes, in terms of wealth and treasure found. Yes, in terms of conquest, for nothing had been conquered. No, in terms of human resources, for the Indians Coronado met were to be the incentive that would bring the Spaniard back to New Mexico.

6

MESA TOP PUEBLO

While the Spaniard did seek gold and glory, he also burned with a missionary zeal and sought souls for his deep-running religion, Roman Catholicism.

For fifty-five years after Coronado, interest in New Mexico and the Southwest was spotty. Other things occupied the Spanish—primarily silver discoveries in the central valleys of Mexico. But men did not forget New Mexico and saw there an opportunity for missionary activity and exploitation. Also, other nations of Europe were beginning to take an interest in the North American continent, and New Mexico began to look attractive to the Spanish as a frontier defensive outpost. The frontier·line pushed ever northward from central Mexico. By 1595, the Spanish were ready to push a salient into New Mexico.

From among the mining communities of northern Mexico, a force of two hundred colonists was assembled by Don Juan Oñate who had a contract to colonize New Mexico. After countless delays due to politics and supply shortages, the Oñate expedition left Chihuahua in 1598. The route went north across the desert to the Rio Grande near El Paso del Norte (modern Juarez), thence up the Rio Grande into New Mexico. On August 18, 1598, they arrived at San Juan, and there founded the first capital of New Mexico, San Juan de los Caballeros. These lands of the Southwest so long colored by the Indian now received a new imprint, one that would alter the direction and flow of culture and change it from the Indian to the Spanish Southwest.

From San Juan, and later (1610) from Santa Fe, Oñate, his men, and his colonists brought New Mexico under the Spanish yoke. In co-operation with the Franciscan Order, which had been assigned the task of con-

7

verting the Indian, Oñate supervised the building of missions and mission churches at many of the pueblos of New Mexico. At the same time, Spanish towns developed, the most important being the new capital at Santa Fe. By 1628, New Mexico was solidly in the hands of her new masters.

The period from 1628 to 1680 was one of internal conflict and isolation for New Mexico. It lay far out on the frontier, alone and distant from its source of supplies. It lacked many of the items necessary for frontier life, particularly hardware and clothing. Its population was small, and in constant fear of Indian uprising, and its officials were too weak to act with vigor. Finally, there was a lack of genuine interest on the part of the central authorities. All these problems led to internal conflicts between soldier and colonist; between colonist and Indian; between colonist and official; and, perhaps most bitter of all, between church and state. This latter conflict would erupt time after time, openly, and with bitterness and denunciation from both sides. Governors were excommunicated as heretics; Franciscans were accused of all sorts of crimes and improper behavior. This, plus the other conflicts, gave rise to growing disrespect by the Indians for their European conquerors. The superiority of Christianity was questioned by the Indians as they watched the attacks and counterattacks made by priest and governor. The whole system of Spanish rule seemed a mockery. In 1680, the Indians decided their way was best after all and rose in rebellion.

Led by Po-pé from Taos, the various pueblos banded together in a mighty effort to remove the Spanish from traditional Indian lands. For the first time the pueblos came together, united by a single purpose. There were two exceptions; Isleta, just south of Albuquerque, and the Piro villages farther south (Socorro) remained loyal to the Spanish. Up and down the Rio Grande Valley, the Spaniards fell before the pent-up anger of the Indians. Survivors gathered at Santa Fe, but their water supply was cut, and they were forced to retreat south. At Isleta and later at the Piro villages, they received aid before continuing south to El Paso del Norte. With them went their Indian allies from Isleta and Socorro. It was a total defeat for the Spanish, and the Indian again was master of New Mexico.

But not for long, for at El Paso there gathered a force dedicated to revenge for their comrades who had died before the Indian onslaught. Ably led by Diego de Vargas, this expedition moved into New Mexico in 1692. The Indians, who had achieved such unity for the moment in 1680, were again badly divided. De Vargas, instead of having to subdue an alliance, had only to deal with one pueblo at a time. Very quickly New Mexico was returned to a mission area and frontier military post. The Pueblo Indians became permanently subjected to European domination. Their one and only attempt at unity had, in the final analysis, failed.

During the seventeenth and eighteenth centuries, New Mexico was the heart of the Spanish empire in the Southwest. Only in southwestern Arizona, western Texas, and California did the Spanish hold any land other than in the upper Rio Grande Valley of New Mexico. During these centuries, this valley complex played out its dual role of mission area and military outpost. Its only connection with the resources and ideas of the world was a long hazardous road that stretched from Santa Fe to Chihuahua City and then south to Mexico City. This was New Mexico's Royal Road, and over it moved everything needed by soldier, priest, and civilian. The trade was dominated by the merchants of Chihuahua, and New Mexico suffered. The tale of New Mexico during this period was one of poverty, hardship, and warfare. And several vital forces moved across the land.

One of these forces had long been in the Southwest, but latent. The Spanish adopted an Indian word meaning *enemy* to describe it—Apache! The Spanish brought with them domesticated animals which quickly adapted to conditions of the New World and became available to the Indian. Most important was the horse, at least as far as the Apache was concerned. By the early eighteenth century, the Apache, and other groups on the plains, had adapted to the use of the horse. While dangerous as foot soldiers, the Apache became vastly more dangerous as mounted warriors. Whereas they had been satisfied with minor raids against the pueblos and the Spanish holdings prior to 1700, they exploded on a wave of terrorism during the eighteenth century which very nearly drove the Spanish from the frontier. Late in the century, the conflict between the Apache and the Spanish became increasingly bitter. The history of the Southwest became the history of incessant Indian incursions and Spanish attempts to control the raiders. The missions declined and in many instances gave way entirely to the presidio or fort. In New Mexico the military came to dominate the missionary, and only through the heroic efforts of the meager force at the Presidio of Santa Fe did the Spanish manage to hold New Mexico from total collapse. A poor province became poorer, population declined, both among the Spanish and Indian, and the future looked dark indeed.

Far from New Mexico, other forces were stirring which would have a profound effect on the province and the Southwest. Spain and the Spanish empire were in trouble. Spain had failed to develop the supply capability to keep her colonies alive and was forced to spend her wealth in other areas of Europe. After two and a half centuries, the cumbersome and inefficient colonial administrative machinery was breaking down. While Spain's star was descending, other European nations were on the move. England, France, Holland, and Russia were contesting with Spain for control of the New World. England and France were digging in on the east coast of North America; Holland was penetrating the islands of the Caribbean, and Russia was pushing down the Pacific Coast from Alaska. The weakness of Spain and the failure of her colonial government, plus help from Napoleon by way of his invasion of the Iberian Peninsula in 1808, brought about the collapse of the Spanish empire. In America, patriots, inspired by the earlier success of the American Revolution and afire with the ideas of the French Revolution, struck out at the remnants of Spanish rule. By 1825, all the Spanish colonies but the islands of the Caribbean were free and independent nations. New Mexico and the Southwest became part of the Mexican state.

9

Almost immediately, Mexico, without leaders, without a political heritage to lead it to stability, and torn by power struggles large and small, was plunged into a period of political anarchy and civil war which would last for half a century. The problems and dangers of a far-flung frontier were lost in the din of conflict, and New Mexico became a forgotten province. Its claims as a mission area were so weak as to be almost nonexistent. It was no longer needed as a military outpost, for the danger to Mexico was not external, but internal. Its reasons for being were forgotten, at least for the moment, and New Mexico had to survive on her own initiative. But for one very important fact, the Spanish salient into the Southwest might have collapsed under the weight of poverty and Indian attacks. That fact was the opening of the Santa Fe Trail in 1821, a trail which linked the Spanish world with the Anglo-Saxon world then pushing its frontiers out from Missouri. This trail, so rich in lore and adventure, so much a part of the history of both the American west and the Spanish north, was the door through which passed the characters for the final act in the history of the Southwest.

Before the final act, however, it is vital and necessary to set down the contribution of two hundred fifty years of Spanish occupation and rule. The coming of the Spaniard to the Southwest began a mixture of white and red races which resulted in a new mixed race. The first generation of those who came up from Mexico were Caucasians; their descendants were usually not. They came seeking wealth and security, but there was neither wealth nor security in New Mexico, and they remained poor, very poor. The society that evolved was to be based upon farming and stock raising, and its organization was to be feudal in nature. There would be no education; hence, there could be no intellectual advance. The world began to go ahead of the people of New Mexico. Only in the house of the rico was there any sign of the wealth and grandeur of Spain; everywhere else was poverty. Farming was left in the hands of the Indian, while the Spaniard chose to be a man on horseback, a cattleman, an aristocrat. In the final analysis, Spanish New Mexico would not develop as democratic and agricultural, but aristocratic and feudal. The hacienda was a part of old Spain in exile. The rico tried vainly to hold to his idea of chivalry and to a decorum suitable to his position. But what chance was there in the face of the increasing poverty, the constant danger to life and property, and time that did not move? While individual courage of the upper class remained, discipline and industry died. When the American army marched into the Southwest, the sons of the *conquistadores* could offer no armed resistance. Perhaps the most amazing thing about the society of the ricos in New Mexico was that it failed to contribute any lasting monument. It left no art, no music, no great highways, no adequate governmental system.

But many elements of Spanish culture were to persist, and these arose from the collective consciousness of the people of New Mexico. Around the great haciendas were small villages with their artisans and workers. It was among these people that the heritage of Spain clung to this land.

10

OLD MISSION CHURCH AT ISLETA PUEBLO

Many of these towns yet remain and are not much different from those of two hundred years ago. To a large degree, their Spanish culture seems hidden and undiscovered, but the people, their loves and hates, pleasures and hopes, beliefs and fears, are governed by tradition, a tradition that finds its roots deep in the soil of Spain.

Today, when we look at the cultural scene in New Mexico, we can see direct evidence of Spanish occupation. The language of half the people in the state is Spanish, in some areas still the Spanish of the sixteenth century. Roman Catholicism, of which the Spanish were the most Catholic, dominates the religious scene. The Spanish heritage in political attitudes, in building and architecture, and in the legal tradition of the state is apparent. New Mexico, of all the states in the United States, is the only one that can claim a truly Spanish heritage.

ANGLO–AMERICAN VIGOR

While Spain lost its empire and New Mexico and the Southwest sank into poverty and decay, yet another force was on the march, a force that welled up in an Anglo–American people clinging to the Atlantic Coast of North America. As these people developed a nation, they also discovered a sense of destiny which turned their faces to the west and their footsteps toward the sunset. With them moved their culture. At first, it was a trickle, a few traders bent on profit, crossing the plains on the Santa Fe Trail. Then the trickle became a flood. For New Mexico, these men came as saviors. The Missouri traders broke the Chihuahua monopoly and

11

goods from all parts of the world began to flow into New Mexico, resulting in higher standards of living. These Yankee traders, sensing a good
thing, also penetrated the markets of Mexico, using New Mexico's Royal
Road to gain entrance.

Again there was conflict, not Spanish and Indian, but Latin and
Anglo–American. Mexico owned the lands of the Southwest and intended
to keep them. But this American, with his gaze glued on western skies,
refused to turn aside, and he strode on, grinding the feeble efforts of
Mexican resistance into the desert sands. The Mexican War in 1846, suddenly transferred ownership of Texas, New Mexico, Utah, Nevada, Arizona, and California from Mexico to the United States. This was nearly
half the territory of Mexico. New Mexico, with her already complex cultural pattern, was subjected to still another influence.

The history of the American occupation of the Southwest is as complex
and diverse as its predecessors. Its ingredients include cattle, mining, railroads, agriculture, science, and the Indian. All these, and others, combined
to give an Anglo–American slant to the Southwest. The Indian culture
did not disappear, nor did the Spanish, but rather a new stratum was cast
that was to complete the mosaic.

When the American arrived in New Mexico, he found a poor, backward area, hungry for trade and outside contacts. He found the Indians
of the Southwest in open rebellion against the white men. The Navajo
and other Apache groups, the Comanche, and some of the Pueblos were
the primary offenders. This was to be the main problem occupying the
time and energy of the American settler and soldier for forty years after
1846. Until the Indian situation was stabilized, there would be little economic and social development.

The method evolved for containing the vicious raids against friendly
Indian, Spanish, and American communities was a series of forts placed
at strategic passes or trails surrounding the traditional lands of the Apache.
The Indian strongholds were located primarily in the mountainous regions
of southwestern New Mexico and southeastern Arizona. The line of forts
stretched along the Rio Grande south of Socorro to the vicinity of Las
Cruces, and west along the southern edge of the mountain escarpment
into Arizona. Then the defense complex ran north across the desert to an
irregular line running east from Flagstaff through Gallup and back to the
Rio Grande. These forts were well garrisoned and provisioned and began
to carry the fight to the Indian. Early success was halted by the conflict
generated by the American Civil War.

The center of the Civil War in the west was in New Mexico. There was
conflict, argument, and some small degree of fighting in other western
states and territories as settlers from the north or south struggled to carry
this territory or that state into the Union or the Confederacy. These were,
however, local matters and as much political as military. In New Mexico,
there was a war and there were battles, battles which deserve to be a part
of the general Civil War story but that are usually forgotten in the smoke
and roar of eastern cannon.

Two major battles were fought in New Mexico, the first a Confederate victory, the second a Union victory which saved New Mexico, and the west, for the Union. The aim of the Confederate forces was to capture, intact if possible, the forts in New Mexico and Arizona with their great store of military provisions, provisions badly needed by the Confederate army. Also, there was a feeling among southern leaders that success in New Mexico might also lead to success in California, badly split on the question of secession, and in Colorado, rich in silver and gold. An army recruited in Texas and commanded by General Henry Sibley was sent to accomplish Confederate aims.

This army entered New Mexico along the traditional route, moving up the Rio Grande from El Paso. It quickly subdued the forts and Union troops in southern New Mexico and continued up-river. On February 21, 1862, it met a Union army commanded by Colonel E. R. S. Canby at Valverde, a small community about twenty miles south of Socorro, New Mexico. Kit Carson, New Mexico's famous trapper and scout, commanded the New Mexico Volunteers, a part of the Union force. Canby's troops were beaten and dispersed at the Battle of Val Verde, leaving the upper Rio Grande Valley virtually without defense. Within a few weeks, the Texans had taken Albuquerque and Santa Fe. But one stronghold in New Mexico remained in the hands of the Union forces. Fort Union, northeast of Las Vegas, New Mexico, became the focal point of action by both north and south. Sibley, marching from Santa Fe, knew success depended on the fall of Fort Union. The Union forces, equally aware of the importance of the fort, hurriedly reinforced it with a number of volunteers from Colorado.

Within Fort Union, a crisis developed over differing opinions on strategy. The fort commander wanted to keep the garrison at full strength and fight the Confederates from within the fort. The Colorado Volunteers wanted to go out and meet the enemy. The latter won and a Union force moved into the passes of the Sangre de Cristo Mountains to meet the Confederates in a fateful battle that would decide control of the west. It was fought at Glorieta Pass on March 28, 1862. Despite the fact that the two armies met on this field, the contest was not decided there. Early on the morning of March 28, a force of 400 Colorado Volunteers, commanded by Colonel John M. Chivington, began a flanking action in hopes of hitting the Confederate rear. This group moved out of the Pass into the mountains, and by a very difficult route moved back toward the Pass behind the Confederate force. On a ridge overlooking Apache Canyon, they saw below them the entire Confederate supply train and cavalry horse herd. In a lightning hit-and-run attack, the supply train and horses were destroyed. When word of this reached Sibley at Glorieta Pass, there was little for him to do but to retire from the field. The Confederate force never recovered from this disaster and gradually retreated to Santa Fe, then back down the Rio Grande into Texas.

With the end of the Civil War, New Mexico and the Southwest returned, not to peace, but to war, war against the Apache. It took twenty years for the American with all his modern weapons and tactics to bring the Apache under control. For the Apache, it ended on September 3, 1886, when Geronimo and his few ragged followers surrendered to General Miles in Skeleton Canyon, Arizona. Under the weight of steel and increasing numbers of white men, the Apache was doomed. Though civilization would swallow the Apache, as it has always succeeded against the barbarian, the Apache made a spectacular defense of his lands and his way of life against both Spaniard and American. He made himself master of the desert, and only the gods of science succeeded in overcoming him and his desert gods.

INDUSTRIAL BOOM

With the Indian situation settled, New Mexico underwent a boom in two important areas, mining and cattle raising. These industries, so much a part of the history of the American West, did and still play an important role in the well-being of the Southwest. Mining camps sprang up along the mountain fringes as new discoveries of silver and gold came to light. Around Socorro and Magdalena, in the Mogollon Mountains, at Hillsboro and Kingston in the Black Range, and hundreds of other places in New Mexico and the Southwest, men hungry for quick wealth swarmed over the hills and mountains and built their roaring camps. While miners were tapping the subsurface wealth, cattlemen were staking out their claims to the grasslands, both on the eastern plains and in the high mountain meadows. Cattle empires grew to staggering proportions, sometimes erupting into violent conflict over grazing and water rights, such as the Lincoln County War made famous by the participation of Billy the Kid.

FEATURE OF THE OLD WEST

The character of the Southwest still bears the stamp of the miner and the cattleman. Although the cattle and grazing industry has declined, as has the traditional mining camp, the past importance of these activities has had a tremendous impact upon the character of Southwest folklore, law, and music and on the thought of the people.

Other influences affected New Mexico as a result of the American occupation, things inherent in the American culture. Ribbons of steel across a continent, buildings of steel and stone, business and commerce, technology, common law, the English language, the Protestant religion, and, above all, the American-brought driving desire to dominate, to win. Certainly the American had to adapt his culture to the desert lands, but he did it in his own way, not in the way of the Indian or Spaniard. So Anglo–American culture became superimposed upon a Spanish culture that was superimposed upon an Indian culture.

Disinherited, that is the word that best describes contemporary New Mexico culture. A stronger race came and took away the inheritance of the Indian, though there did result a blood mixture. Only in superficial matters did the Spanish adopt any of the Indian ways. The Spanish, too, succumbed to a stronger people and have been denied the privilege commonly accorded to conquered peoples, that of mixing their blood with that of the conquerors. One finds today in New Mexico three distinct people—Indian, Spanish, and Anglo–American—as sharply contrasted as the strands in a Navajo blanket. There is pure red alongside white, and only rarely do the colors blend into pinks or grays. This is why we must say that New Mexico is a mosaic, not a synthesis, of many elements, clearly defined.

Across the span of time, great men, people, and ideas have molded New Mexico and Southwest history. Indian, Spanish, American—vital forces that are today working toward a genuinely unique culture in New Mexico. The modern world may well give to the Southwest the idea or catalyst that will blend these elements into a single force. Science, techniques, ideas are things of the present and are for the present to assess and synthesize. The Indian gods of air, earth, and sky and the white man's gods of morality and science do not differ a great deal in their aspirations for their chosen people, and perhaps they will decree a splendid and unique synthesis from the cultural mosaic. Through understanding comes knowledge; from knowledge, creation.

The Exotic Plants of New Mexico

by ROSS CALVIN

The problem of discussing plant life becomes complicated, for some of those arriving in New Mexico may be compound microscope botanists, some collectors, others pathologists, still others geneticists. Some will be chemists or mathematicians, some others untrained in the ways of growing things and mainly interested in seeing while they tour. But one thing is fairly certain—most visitors will come from a distance, so it may be useful to invite them to observe what they can readily see on the way hither, which will be a relatively painless method of amassing some information.

Yet the method of arrival itself suggests choices, options, and exercises in probability. Do visitors come in covered wagons, or in jet planes; by bus, car, train, or some other way? The most convenient way, doubtless, is by plane traveling six hundred miles an hour at a height of some thirty thousand feet; but the most rewarding way is by saddle or on foot as the early collectors came.

Since one cannot know his own country well if he knows no other, a visitor from the east arriving at an altitude of five miles will probably be more conscious than others of drastic changes in the landscape when he first looks down on New Mexico. Instead of the universal green of the east, he will note the earth as an unaccustomed tawny, reddish brown expanse, and this will be its common color through most months of the year. He will note the absence of rivers, but the presence of mountains which generally ring the horizon. He will wonder, after traversing the border counties at the western edge of the Great Plains, at the infrequency of plowlands, and will promptly conclude that New Mexico is one vast, bare desert—an impression that will be corrected rapidly when he visits the dark National Forests where the slim, crowded spruces and firs tower skyward.

The visitor from El Paso, as the Chihuahua desert (the name is fairly deserved) slides backward underneath him, will be amazed at the serpentine stripe of vivid verdure below, all completely leveled, and all marked off by geometrical lines and tightly bordered by pale hills where the vegetation is reduced to tiny dots not tall enough to cast a shadow. Still proceeding north, he will presently be above a ninety-mile stretch where the vegetation is so skimpy and the river so closely boxed in by desolate hills that Spanish explorers bestowed on it the sinister name *Jornada del Muerto*—Dead Man's Journey, which is self-explanatory.

But on the other hand, a visitor descending into New Mexico from the northland in wintertime above this same Rio Grande will traverse a featureless jumble of peaks on which the black coniferous forest no longer shows as black at all but, snow-encased, gleams as white as the naked snow-fields themselves. And he will find incredible the immense range of climate spanned in a flight only an hour long.

The jet traveler approaching from the west beholds the greatest, most spectacular panorama of all, the true wasteland of the desert, with vast blocks uplifted from out of earth's crust, plateaus dissected by giant empty canyons whose walls are seared to utter nudity by ages of the most intense sunshine on our continent. Here the architecture of nature is all designed on a gigantic scale, and the climate exhibits influences of a mighty ocean, of towering mountain chains, and the range of wandering planetary winds which created the desert. From the altitude of a cruising jet, the distances, the speed, the color, and the light are indescribably exhilarating.

Since the traveler arriving from any direction can see for identification only a few species, it will suffice to point out only two of the harbingers of eastern New Mexico, both of which are dominant on that area of the Great Plains: the blue grama grass, which in fall and winter bears the graceful sickle-shaped head, and the small *Yucca glauca* which cannot be mistaken for anything else.

Along the northern line, the visitor should look for the somber, almost black, forest of spruce and fir with its white patches of aspen on the 10,000-foot slopes. Descending farther southward, even a casual observer will note that these species give way first to the yellow pines, then to the junipers ("cedars") and dwarf pines or piñons. The visitor arriving from the south will find most conspicuous of all the olive-green creosote bush in its summer-winter foliage, next, the omnipresent mesquite (*Prosopis*), then the various *Opuntia* cacti (chollas and prickly pears), and the yuccas.

As he comes in from Arizona, the splendid saguaros will beckon him toward the gateway of New Mexico, but they will nowhere enter it themselves. The vase-shaped body of the ocotillo consisting of unbranching, ten-foot wands should be recognized at a glance, as likewise should the various yuccas and agaves. And in early springtime, a low tree with a rounded mass of golden bloom will joyously proclaim its identity as a paloverde.

The desert plants thus enumerated can be recognized along various stretches of U.S. 66 as one holds his speed at a conservative ninety or, even better, at a conservative sixty.

The amateur scientist will need to do some homework before he learns much systematic botany or plant physiology. It takes considerable study to comprehend the slow, age-long process which has resulted in the evolution of all this grotesque vegetation: the interaction of extreme aridity, high temperature, low humidity, high evaporation, infrequent precipitation, the hostility of numerous chemical solutions, and the natural rapacity of the animal population. Each plant must have an adaptation of its own, from the tiny winter annual, which must race through its course from a tender rosette to ripened seed before the searing sunshine arrives, on up through the series to the stoic saguaro, which seems able to scorn nature's enmity.

17

A final warning to the air traveler. He should be sure before deplaning that he has observed a *bajada*. It is a must. Bajada is one name, outwash slope is another, alluvial fan is still another. The stewardess should inquire of each student, and if his answer is "no," she should reply, "Then you've just flunked the course." A bajada is the most characteristic single feature of all in the sloping, stony topography of the desert—and remember that the surface of the desert is regularly sloping and stony. The Spanish word itself means only a down slope, but it has come to have a semitechnical sense—a fan-shaped apron of rocky debris at the foot of a mountain where it has settled out of the summer torrents and there keeps accumulating in successive floods. As the mass builds up, the bigger fragments drop out closest to the parent crag, then the small ones, finally the coarse gravel, and lowest of all on the slope the fine sand. Thus the fragments are graduated in size, in distance traveled, and in the nature of soil resulting. As the fan increases in size and laps up higher and higher on the mountain's flank, the geologists often describe the result by saying that the mountain "is burying itself under its own debris." From the air, the lines of drainage will be seen to have assumed the form of a tree with its trunk downward, its branches high in air. But the most interesting aspect of a bajada is the nice proportion which nature works out between the plant species and their location on the curve.

FROM SAGEBRUSH TO SPRUCE TREES

The traveler who has viewed the Southwestern panorama of nature from its sagebrush to its spruce trees has indeed seen most of it. The spruce which grows wild only well up on the higher mountains is familiar to everybody because it has become a favorite in formal planting everywhere. But the sages—who knows them? To the tenderfoot, almost any gray plant is "sage." To my friends the cowmen, sage means commonly saltbush. To my friends the foresters, sage means an artemisia. But there are romantics to whom "purple sage" is Apache plume, which is a member of the wild rose family.

Some popular education would seem to be desirable. And this applies, too, to the cacti, for there is more misinformation about them than anything else that grows, runs, or creeps—except rattlesnakes. The clever people who design travel folders and pictorial maps almost always put saguaros in New Mexico. But saguaros do not grow in New Mexico. That is final! And the yucca is not a cactus. That also is final. Nor yet the ocotillo—that defiant, splendid denizen of the desert which flaunts the scarlet torch of flowers. The question that is always on the surface as one writes of plant life in the Southwest is, "Who wants to know?" The picnicker wants to know the names—and nothing much besides—of the wild flowers. My friend the cowman already has the names; that is, the common ones. If I chance to mention blue grama grass, he gently corrects me, "black grama." Then if I mention black grama, he says, "no, white grama." But at least he is concerned about something more important than

18

nonscientific names. He wants to know if the plant is some
lean old cow can eat, whether it stays green in winter, and if .
the soil in place. The tourist who pilots car and passengers som,
dred miles between breakfast and bedtime asks only what he wa,
at. The rest of us who go into the mountains often enough to be in,
by the layer-cake succession of plants on their slopes can, with the
some reading, amass a store of knowledge where others amass only
age. On a tour, it is mileage or knowledge. One has to choose.

Actually, our New Mexico desert is not dominated by sage. That honor
is held by the creosote bush, called by some of the old-timers *greasewood*,
Covillea glutinosa, by some of the scientists—along with five other
synonyms. Like the mesquite with which it shares the same general habitat
but *does not intermix*, it occupies an immense spread of territory, roughly
from Texas to California. Since no livestock will eat it and the ground
it occupies is equally useless for agriculture because of aridity and stoni-
ness, creosote is a veritable coyote for survival. The traveler descending
from Taos to Santa Fe need not look for it. The sage of that locality,
which gives the landscape its singularly mournful aspect, is a true sage.
With good reason the cowboys call it *black sage*.

In 1846, Lieutenant Emory, as he rode southward with the Army of
the West, first encountered the creosote as he approached Socorro. The
northward extension of the plant is at the same point today, and the range
of mesquite extends only a few miles farther north. These two remarkable
plants are the main markers of the Lower Sonoran Zone. In the same
arid, stony, broken country, the traveler will find an abundance of cacti,
and these plants are usually supposed to be the most tenacious of all
tenacious growing things. Actually, in southwestern Arizona and neighboring parts of California there are whole areas where the aridity is too severe
for cacti, but for our state—let it stand. Everybody, of course, has noted
the grotesque shape of the plants, but not everybody has noted that the
shape was chosen with a canny intelligence. A globe exposes less surface
(that is, the vulnerable area for evaporation) than any other solid of equal
volume. And a cylinder is second best. Another thing—cacti being suc-
culents are filled with a watery sap or juice which quickly coagulates after
a wound and stops the waste of moisture. Furthermore, the plant's aggres-
sive root system is arranged so as to capture the ground's scanty moisture
most quickly and completely after rains.

Cacti of more than sixty species occur within our state, but more than
nine tenths of the plants seen along the highway—unless they are brought
together for a garden collection—can be grouped into one genus, the
Opuntia. The family likeness is shown not by the shape or general ap-
pearance but by the fact that all are jointed. Both the cane cactus (also
called cholla and elkhorn) and the pancaked prickly pear, unlike the big
barrel cactus and the numerous small species which resemble it in shape,
have joints and may therefore be rightly called opuntias. The "pancakes,"
it may be remarked, are not leaves but divisions of the stem. A cactus
gets along without leaves. So a good rough-and-ready test is this: if it has

aves, it is not a cactus—which eliminates ocotillo, yucca, agave, sotol, and so on.

The barrel cactus is sure to be seen growing beside service stations in the southern part of the state. Its name as well as its size identifies it. The flowers and the large lemon-shaped fruits are worth a glance. If they do not occur on the south side of the plant, it has been transplanted *and turned.* The evidence is as trustworthy as the presence of moss on the north side of a tree in the forest.

The barrel cacti, the opuntias, acacias, the ocotillos, along with the creosote and mesquite already mentioned, have a way of growing along together in what is called a plant society. These all belong in the bottom layer of the cake called the Lower Sonoran Zone, which is best seen on the Rio Grande mesas near El Paso.

The layer next above it comprises the foothill country of the Upper Sonoran Zone, which includes most of the state of New Mexico. Some of its common markers are juniper, piñon, oak of various species including live oak, mountain mahogany, mescal, yucca, beargrass, and the famous blue grama grass. It is exhibited all along the Continental Divide in the southwest part of the state but nowhere so well as in the Fort Bayard Reservation. There a tract, protected for three generations from wood-cutting, fires, and intensive grazing, offers a large-scale picture of the lovely land that once was New Mexico. There the character and amount of vegetation astounds the visitor who is familiar with only the close-picked, parched aspect of the landscape that generally borders the main highways. When seen from the air, the very color of the grass-mantled earth is many shades lighter than that of the bare overgrazed ranges a few miles to the south. And the difference can be seen by anybody.

The foothills are dotted, not covered, with juniper and piñon. The dwarfed, rounded little junipers (properly enough called cedars) leave the traveler unprepared to believe that they will anywhere become respectable forest trees. Yet in the Burro Mountains, the alligator-bark species, finest of them all, reaches a diameter of five feet and an age of about 1000 years. The wood has an extraordinary fragrance, and its smoke tells the neighbors for blocks around that you are warming yourself at the fireplace. Another notable thing about the wood is its resistance to decay in the earth. I have removed pieces of it from subterranean ruins of the Mimbres culture which, according to the best archaeological opinion, are some eight hundred years old.

The yuccas deserve a story by themselves. One small, unimpressive species greets you on the meadows at the foot of Raton Pass; others have to be searched out along high limestone ridges where the foothills are deciding to become mountains. The one chosen for our state flower is the tall yucca (*Yucca elata*), a superb species best seen along the Continental Divide near Silver City. The genus reaches its greatest size in the grotesque Joshua tree, which never fails to attract the eye on the Mohave desert in California.

The century plant has a name that always gets attention. But let us

Yucca plants

be sure we mean the same thing. Rightly, it means the mescal, the favorite food of the Mescalero Apaches. Besides these two names, it is called also maguey and, no doubt, Spanish dagger along with various other spine-tipped plants. All of which clinches the argument for a name which for all users is a certain designation for one object and only one. It is not just because botanists like to appear learned that they call this plant *Agave parryi*. That title is as descriptive as middle *C* for one key on the piano, and in the same way international.

Everyone inquires about the century plant's life expectancy. An insurance man might make an inference from the name. The plant is a big compact cluster or rosette of rigid, upward-pointing, spadelike leaves, each four or five inches in width and each tipped with a vicious, stout thorn. Year after year the plant just sits there by a boulder, unnoticed. I question whether anything alive on the desert has a better life expectancy. As far as my observations go, it has no diseases. It is invincible to drouth. Freezing does not harm it, and fire cannot burn it— although a yucca even when green will flame up like a torch. No hungry old cow can crop it, and no rodent gnaws it, at least not enough to do harm. And since the Indians have gone on reservations, no human uses it. So it stays there.

In fact, nothing less than a caterpillar can leave a dent on it—not, of course, the caterpillar that eats young tomato plants, but the Caterpillar that pulls heavy road machinery. The plant just does not die before maturity, it would seem. A remarkable organism, indeed! But after many, many years, depending on the amount of moisture it receives, it makes up its mind to flower. In one tremendous effort, it shoots up a twelve-foot flower stalk at the rate of several inches a day. The blossoming is a final, dramatic, beautiful gesture, for by the time the flowers have withered, the great tenacious plant has turned to a ghastly purple and is dead.

On the high slopes where the last yuccas end and only a few junipers remain in the race for survival, the yellow pines come in to mark off what is called the Transition Zone. The pines need no description, no printed promotion. The traveler, any traveler, can appreciate them although he might not be stirred to the slightest interest by the lovely yuccas. Since the beginning of time, the pines, fragrant, cheerful, companionable, have been man's best friend. Among the ponderosa pines takes place most of the hunting, most of the camping, much of the picnicking. There is no

PINON NEEDLES

danger that the tourist will overlook the pine belt and the pines for they are probably the most numerous tree in New Mexico.

Above them, the classifications are less clearly defined and ecologists are less inclined to agree on zonation. The Canadian Zone, if we settle on that name, occurs only in small areas on the map, and most of them north of Santa Fe. These are high ridges and island peaks that tower high enough to tempt the Engelmann spruces. Yet some of these islands occur as far south as the Mogollon Mountains and thus bring Canadian Zone scenes almost to the Mexican border. For hardy ecologists who want to explore high ridges and horns of bare stone which rise as clean as a hound's tooth clear up into the Arctic-alpine Zone, it is necessary to enter Colorado.

Engelmann spruce forests may be associated with the 10,000-foot level. The blue spruce is very similar, perhaps only a subspecies, but it comes in a little lower. The Engelmann makes a dense forest hardly allowing invaders, but the blue is more tolerant, less austere. It loves the water and is the natural companion of chill, cascading trout streams. Though fond of shadow, it seems to grow equally well where the narrow canyons widen and admit the sunshine upon the tiny meadows of lush grass, cranesbill, velvety red cinquefoils, lupines, and yellow columbines. And when one of these miniature openings is fringed with spruces whose pointed tips rise sharp against a curtain of azure with its white cumulus clouds, there you have the loveliest vista in the mountains.

OUR VISIBLE IMPACT ON THE PLANT LIFE

Though nature lovers usually find the life zones more fascinating than any other aspect of plants in the mountains, there is one other much more important. It is the misuse, injury, and destruction of native plant life. Because scientists are generally alert to the conservation of what is use-

22

ful and beautiful in natural resources, I venture to bring up the matter here.

A useful case history is provided by Silver City, New Mexico. It was founded in the early seventies as a silver camp, which would fairly guarantee a certain amount of reckless haste and rowdy carelessness. Point two was its location on a foothill watershed only twenty-seven square miles in area. Point three was an extreme concentration of livestock near the town. Point four was the fact that the annual rainfall was crowded mainly into July, August, and a part of September.

Mines are naturally users of timber. Obviously, shafts and tunnels have to be timbered. More than that, little smelters nestled back among the hills were also hungry for wood. And since coal was expensive and hard to get, most of the adobe cottages were heated many years by juniper, oak, and piñon firewood. All these matters were naturally, if not actually, inevitable under the circumstances.

The massive ore wagons and freight wagons had to be drawn by four- to ten-horse teams—and the horses kept on eating. Then because it was also a ranching country, each cowboy had to keep a *remuda* of saddle horses—and they ate too. Also, the few cows that provided milk for the children grazed hungrily over the stony slopes. Most of all, the range cattle, which had no provender at all except that which the competitive, half-starved steers could provide for themselves, overgrazed every square foot of pasturage down to the bare soil. The government's open-range policy made overgrazing inevitable because no ranchman could protect his pasturage since it was all unfenced. The cow that got there first got the grass. That passed as land management, which proves that some statesmen then were about as wise as some of the Wizards of Washington now. But the advent of fences caused the cutting of millions of fence posts where none should have been cut.

When the grass went, its roots went, and when its roots went, there was nothing to hold the soil, and then it, too, started to go. And go it did.

Elk

A deep hole formed in Main Street, as it is still called on the Silver City town plat. The best explanation I can find of that hole is that earth was taken out of it to form adobe bricks for the walls of houses and corrals (that clay did make good adobe!). Meanwhile, the woodhaulers' wagons had greedily carted away the trees from each little canyon, while the narrow steel tires cut deep ruts which formed two deep gullies at the first heavy rain. Then the parallel gullies proceeded to wash out deeper and create a middle ridge or high center on which axles got stuck. Since there was nobody responsible for making a new road, there was no choice except to move over and form another track and use it until in turn it became unusable. (By this simple kind of destruction, the old Santa Fe Trail, it is said, reached a width of a hundred feet.)

But the water descending the slope kept increasing its destructive velocity as the denuded ground approached the bareness of a tin roof. Villagers observed that the hole in their Main Street was becoming a waterfall after each rain, and that the ruin was passing into a big-time operation. The town built a dam to restrain the floods. It washed out in the first one. Soon Main Street followed it down the drain, which by this time was already a hideous gash in the earth many miles long and twenty feet deep. Then the water began on a really different scale of destruction. One furious flood washed away the cabin in which Billy the Kid's mother lived. More than that, it washed away the wall of Judge Newcomb's house and abducted his Steinway from the second floor. A few yards from the spot, an old photograph taken in 1891 shows a woodhauler's ox team lying in the street there. It gives no hint at that time of the famous Big Ditch—the only name that Main Street, Silver City has had now for the last forty years.

By 1927, after many other attempts had been made to tame the floods, a steel bridge about one hundred feet long and thirty feet above the floor of the "canyon" was swung into place. In 1935-1936, the Soil Conservation Service went to work in earnest, made the watershed a demonstration area, and spent a third of a million dollars there in a short time.

In the *New Mexico Magazine* for August 1934, the really incredible story of the Big Ditch is exactly documented with old photographs and newspaper clippings. After a friendship of many years with old-time miners and ranchers at Silver City, I would not point an accusing finger at one of them. I appeal, however, for a greater vigilance over plant life and soils nowadays from everybody. In such protected areas as the Fort Bayard Reservation, the U.S. National Forest enclosures, and the frontier cemeteries, the imagination can visualize a New Mexico that is far different from what is here today—a close-picked, hard-used land where unwise woodcutting has continued through much of the last three centuries and where the thin ranges have been required to support in the last century alone perhaps more than one hundred million cows, sheep, and horses. The magnitude of the cause accounts for the magnitude of the effect.

A good many years ago, I wrote as the concluding paragraph to *Sky Determines* what seemed to some exaggerated praise for my adopted homeland. There is now less and less cavil from any readers. I believed the words true in 1934, and I stand my ground now.

Perhaps nowhere in the world is the natural setting nobler than in New Mexico — more beautiful with spacious desert, sky, mountain; more varied in rich, energizing climate, more dramatic in its human procession, more mellow with age-old charm. Endowed with sunshine that stimulates, and winter chill that toughens; with silence and majestic desert color that offer a spiritual companionship, it has enough. Here, if anywhere is air, earth, sky fit to constitute a gracious homeland, not alone for those who study and create, but as well for those who play, for those who sit still to brood and dream.

Tyuonyi Pueblo ruin

This large ruin in Bandelier National Monument lies along the banks of El Rito de los Frijoles. Narrow-leaf cottonwoods line the stream, and shrubs of the Upper Sonoran Zone cover the hillside slopes.

Dwellers in the Hills and Plains

by LEVON LEE*

The vast sweep of New Mexico's 77 million acres, which ranges all the way from the Alpine tundra of the tallest mountains down to the heat of the lower Sonoran desert, offers a home and sanctuary for many kinds of wild life.

Some of these animals are considered game animals; others may be pests, since they prey upon or destroy what mankind regards as its own. The coyote which takes a sheep from the small herder is wicked indeed in the eyes of the sheepman. Predatoriness on all living things by other living things has gone on since time began and will continue—mankind being not the least predator.

A good definition is that composed by the late Judge C. M. Botts who defined a predator as "a critter that takes another critter that I want."

New Mexico's immense topographic and geologic differences make for a very wide range of habitats preferred by the various species. The elk and deer, being highly adaptable, may be found from the Alpine tundra of the higher mountains clear out into the creosote desert. Deer occur in four separate subspecies: the Rocky Mountain and the desert mule deer, the western whitetail, and the Sonoran fantail deer, which is also a whitetail. These animals may be found all the way from the dense coniferous forests of the north with perpetual gloom and cold to the sun-scorched granite mountains such as the Florida and the Organ mountains of southern New Mexico; from great towering granite spires to the folded blocks of limestone such as comprise the Big Hatchets, the Guadalupe, and the San Andres mountains.

The javelina, or little wild pig, lives along the watercourses in the southwest part of the state. Its thin spiky hair gives it little or no protection against cold, and only in the balmier parts of New Mexico does it feel at home.

The desert bighorn sheep, as distinguished from his cousin the Rocky Mountain bighorn, goes around on a sun-scorched, ocotillo-covered limestone-rubble slope in the full glare of the sun and lies down to take his afternoon siesta. The Rocky Mountain bighorn, on the other hand, with his preference for cooler climates does not shun even the dense spruce timber at the very top of the Sandia Mountains as the hideout for his afternoon rest.

This adaptability by New Mexico's species to the tremendous differences in altitude, rainfall, and temperature makes them all the more valuable as a resource for the pleasure and enjoyment of everyone.

---

* New Mexico Department of Game and Fish.

PACK TRAIN ON A WILDERNESS TRAIL

27

The most popular big game animals in New Mexico are the mule deer in either of the two subspecies. Every fall, beginning in late October and extending ordinarily through December, more than 100,000 hunters take to the woods for their 50-50 chance of bringing home the sought-after mule deer. A hunter may shoot his mule deer at the Alpine tundra timber line, out in the blazing heat of the creosote desert, or among the rock crags of some of the southern desert mountains. He will find his quarry a worthy opponent. Shy, wild, and with terrific eyesight and hearing, these animals provide a true challenge.

Elk and antelope, as well as bighorn sheep, are hunted by special licenses only, since their numbers do not warrant a general open season. These special licenses are much sought after and are ordinarily made available by application and a public drawing in the fall. The javelina, confined to our southwestern counties, is also hunted by special license. It is noteworthy that although New Mexico had protected them for many years, the javelina did not increase its numbers. As a matter of fact, the natural losses applied against any game species are going to be in effect no matter whether hunting is permitted or not, the hunting being merely subtracted from what would be lost to nature anyhow.

Our state mammal, the black bear, is found throughout the wooded areas of the state and occasionally wanders out into the plains or down into the desert mountains of the south. Bears are hunted avidly in the fall by sportsmen with dog packs before the regular big game seasons begin, when the use of dogs is prohibited. They are again hunted during the big game seasons by anyone bearing the proper license, but no packs of dogs are allowed. This is to prohibit the possibility of dogs being used to pursue elk, deer, or wild turkey, an illegal act in New Mexico.

New Mexico is fortunate in having a tremendous diversity of both upland game and waterfowl, and big game and small game for her people. Importantly, the game resources are spread out through every county in the state.

The state's richness of bird life is varied and extensive. New Mexico ranks among the first five in the total number of birds found within its boundaries. More than 400 species of birds live within the state. These range all the way from the tiny mites of the bird kingdom, the humming-birds, weighing less than an ounce, to the great white whistling swan, weighing up to 25 pounds, or the Merriam turkey, which may weigh close to 30. Of the six species of quail found in the United States, New Mexico has four and may possess the fifth, since the mountain quail of the western coast have been introduced into this state and still occur on the west slope of the Sacramento Mountains near Tularosa. Five species of doves found throughout the state from the highest coniferous forest down into the scorching heat of the creosote desert are the Inca dove, ground dove, mourning dove, white-winged dove, and the bandtail pigeon, all of them close relatives. Of these, only two, the mourning dove and the white-winged dove, are commonly hunted as game species.

An unexplained and precipitous decline struck the bandtail pigeon about ten or twelve years ago, from which it apparently has never re-covered. Although hunting was undoubtedly part of the pressure exercised against these birds, it in no way accounted for their sudden and dramatic decline in numbers. This decline may gradually be reversed, since more and more of these birds are being seen. It is well known that animals with a high reproductive capacity can endure much heavier losses to their popu-lation than can those with low or very limited reproduction, such as the bandtail, which normally lays only a single egg. The mourning dove, on the other hand, lays two eggs at a time and may raise as many as five or more broods in one year. Take this one step further with the scaled or Gambel quail, which may lay up to 12 or 15 eggs, and it can readily be seen that the population of bandtail pigeons can never endure the losses that the much more prolific mourning dove and quail can. The same might be said by comparison of elk and deer. Elk do not bear their first young until their third year, and then the cow may not bear young but alternate years until her seventh or eighth year; by that time she has begun to de-cline in vigor; in her total life she may not produce more than four or five calves. The mule deer, on the other hand, start bearing at the age of two, with their first birth normally single; from then on, twins are usual for the rest of the doe's life. Thus, deer have a considerably greater reproductive potential than do elk or bighorn sheep, which have one young at a time.

The fleet-footed antelope of the open rolling plains is another example of fairly high reproductive capacity, since they breed earlier than do deer and normally bear twins. Antelope are confined to the more open country where their prodigious running ability and marvelous eyesight stand in good stead in protecting them against their natural enemies.

The wild turkey, classified by law in New Mexico as big game, is found throughout the mountainous areas of the state, not excepting some of the desert ranges. New Mexico is one of two states fortunate enough to possess three of the five forms of the wild turkey known to the United States: the Merriam turkey, found in the higher elevations of the moun-tainous areas, usually the ponderosa forest; the Rio Grande turkey, con-fined to the watercourses of the eastern plains; and the fairly rare Mexican turkey, found in the Animas and Peloncillo mountains of extreme south-western New Mexico. In Hildalgo County these mountains are actually largely Mexican in both flora and fauna. Some of the rarest, most beau-tiful birds of North America are also found in this area and nowhere else in the United States with the exception of southeastern Arizona.

Our most abundant game bird, the mourning dove, is found in every county of the state and nests from the coniferous forests of the north and the higher mountains of the south clear out into the plains where there is not a tree in sight for miles. Doves are extremely adaptable and very prolific. They provide the finest kind of sport shooting and are avidly sought, particularly by shotgun enthusiasts of the eastern and southern parts of the state.

Scaled quail are found throughout New Mexico, being absent only in elevations above 7000 feet. Even there, they periodically occur but are ordinarily driven back by winter snow. Gambel quail are found throughout the river courses of the Rio Grande Valley, the San Juan Valley, and the southwestern watercourses. The Mearns' quail is found in the southern half of the state in the higher mountain elevations, whereas the bobwhite quail occupies the grassy rolling sandhills of the eastern counties where it is commonly found together with scaled quail.

Quail hunting is one of the most popular sports in New Mexico and many thousands of hunters can hardly wait from one season to the next. New Mexico is in the heart of the scaled quail country and provides some of the finest shooting to be had anywhere.

Migratory waterfowl, while not considered abundant, are not uncommon in this state, known more for its aridity than for its rivers and lakes. The two main flyways are the Rio Grande Valley and the Pecos Valley, with the Pecos Valley being somewhat ahead in total numbers.

Ducks commonly found in New Mexico in abundance are teal, both green-winged and blue-winged as well as the lesser-known cinnamon teal, mallards, widgeon, pintails, gadwall, scaups, canvasbacks, redheads, and other species.

In addition, New Mexico plays winter home to many thousands of the lesser sandhill crane which is confined to the river valleys and open plains of the eastern part of the state, particularly the southeastern counties. A smaller population of the greater sandhill crane is found in the Rio Grande Valley and near Columbus. Flocks of the small Richardson's goose are found in the northeastern counties, in particular, and along river courses throughout the state. The small snow goose is likewise confined mostly to major river courses. The larger Canada geese are found particularly in the middle Rio Grande Valley where extensive development has been made by both state and federal agencies to encourage the use and the presence of bands of geese.

New Mexico is unique in that it was the first state in many years to be able to open a hunting season on the lesser sandhill crane. This bird is comparatively abundant, the total population probably being in excess of 200,000, with the vast majority of these birds wintering in west Texas, New Mexico, and Mexico. They occasionally cause heavy depredation to grain crops in the southeastern part of the state, and hunting has been partly justified on the basis that the large wintering flocks might be broken up and depredation spread over a larger area for less individual effect. These birds are tall, wild, and shy. They are hard to hunt, even more so than geese, and although strenuous efforts have been made, not too many of them are bagged.

One should not overlook the tremendous opportunity for sport hunting of unprotected species, such as the various rabbits, the mountain lions and bobcats, and coyotes.

The wolf is now very rare in New Mexico. Only occasionally do wolves come out of Mexico into the southwestern counties, usually in Hidalgo, Luna, and Doña Ana. Wolves are large, effective predators and are incompatible with the cattle-raising industry. Since they have a fondness for beef, the hand of the cattleman is raised against them.

The mountain lion prefers his natural prey of deer, mule deer being the principal victims. The bobcat preys on deer and on many of the small wild animals, rabbits in particular. These predators, when run and hunted with a pack of dogs, provide a fascinating sport which is growing in popularity.

The use of calls to attract animals to a "victim" has become widespread. The calls imitate the distressed cry of rabbits and other creatures which to the predator means a meal close at hand. Everything from mountain lions to red-tailed hawks have been hunted by this procedure, and it can be very successful in bagging quarry. This type of hunting has value in that it can be enjoyed at any time of the year throughout the state and with a minimum of time and effort.

Hunting is a conservation practice that, wisely administered, results in wholesome out-of-door recreation and brings many tons of high protein food of highest quality to the table. Nature nowhere in her economy locks up a resource and throws away the key—we should be no less wise.

Long gone are the buffalo which once roamed the High Plains of eastern New Mexico. Exotic animals, imported and stocked along the rugged canyon of the Canadian River above Conchas Reservoir, are the Barbary sheep with their magnificent coiled horns. Beavers dam some of the mountain streams, badgers and skunks can be seen from the highways, and amid the forests are squirrels and porcupines, while high on rock slopes, the Rocky Mountain woodchuck and the gray rock cony dash from ledge to ledge. The white-tailed ptarmigan also haunts these high crags, and lower down the mountain, bluebirds nest. Hawks, eagles, magpies, jays, ravens, orioles, wrens, sparrows, warblers, finches, and many other birds of endless variety soar over canyon, forest, and sand-dune desert.

Most notable of all is the crested roadrunner, the chapparal cock or paisano of Mexico and the state bird. In between racing with horsemen or automobiles, the slender roadrunner cocks his head, strikes swiftly and victoriously, then swallows his victim, which can be a small rattlesnake, whole.

Snakes there are aplenty. Mostly, they are nonpoisonous, such as the garter snake, glass snake, puff adder, ring-necked snake, the coachwhip, the Mexican blacksnake, and the large western bullsnake. The small but very venomous coral snake is rare, but common among rocks and near streams are the large western diamondback rattlesnake, the prairie rattlers, and the less common green or blacktailed rattlesnake. Every sun-warmed rock has its scampering lizard, and nearby are horned toads, dry-land terrapins, tortoises, tarantulas, centipedes, vinegarroons, scorpions, and spiders. Of these latter desert animals, only the black widow spider is poisonous.

Contrast in the influence of environments is shown by the animals that inhabit the "malpais," the recent flows of black, rough-surfaced lava, compared with similar animals found among the white gypsum dunes of White Sands. Black or darkly colored subspecies of mice, plains wood rats,

SKETCH OF ROADRUNNER, NEW MEXICO STATE BIRD

kangaroo rats, and rock squirrels live on the black lava, whereas white or pale counterparts of these animals live among the white gypsum dunes.

The dwellers in the hills and plains of New Mexico are as varied as the hills and plains; they add their color and movement to the scenes of the Land of Enchantment.

Rocks That Shape the Enchanting Landscape

by FRANK E. KOTTLOWSKI

"As old as the hills." How much more ancient can anything be? Yet New Mexico's hills, its enchanting landscapes, were built in but the most recent "minute" of geologic time. Merely one geologic era ago, marine waters covered the state, and storm-tossed waves ruled where now the hot sun beats down on dry sands and cacti a mile above sea level.

What determined the Land of Enchantment's landscapes? Shaping these land forms are the rocks of the earth's crust, the structure of those rocks, and the endless battle between the rocks and the atmosphere. A story spelled out in stone, the geologic history. The rocks determine.

Eons ago, it began; one billion, two billion, or perhaps even more billions of years ago. A history whose beginnings have been lost owing to destruction of its earliest records. A history, written in the rocks, that is divided into four general parts (fig. 1). The oldest rocks, more than 600 m.y. (million years) old, almost devoid of traces of life, are the Precambrian rocks. The Paleozoic rocks, 230 to 600 m.y. old, are marked by ancient (*paleo-*) life. This was the Period of Invertebrates, animals without backbones. Mesozoic rocks, 70 to 230 m.y. old, formed in the Era of Dinosaurs and contain types of life that are intermediate (*meso-*) between the ancient and modern animals. And rocks of the Cenozoic Era, 70 m.y. ago to the present, make up the latest (*ceno-*, recent) chapter of the earth's history.

Events of the Cenozoic Era have had the greatest influence on New Mexico's landscapes. So let us begin the story at the dawn of the Cenozoic, and return to the earlier geologic chapters later.

CENOZOIC ERA

The mountains, the plains, the rivers, and the lakes all are transitory features of the landscape, created during the recent part of the Cenozoic Era, and all doomed to destruction in the near future, geologically speaking. Even so, some of the plains and mountains may predate man's evolution onto the earth scene.

Gone were the late Mesozoic seas; never again during our lifetime nor the lifetime of many future generations will marine waters roll over New Mexico, and sea-spawned creatures rule. For the first two thirds of the Cenozoic, the Paleogene Period (25 to 70 m.y. ago), New Mexico suffered from the dying effects of the great Laramide upheaval of the earth's crust. Large areas were exposed to the harsh erosion of stream and wind. The landscape looked as parts of southwestern New Mexico do today—tall rugged mountain ranges scattered in isolated patches amid wide gravelly

Figure is a table of geologic time.

Scale of geologic time in millions of years	Era	Geologic age		Rocks	Dominant life
70	CENOZOIC	Neogene	Pleistocene	Bandelier volcanic ash, basalts, sand dunes, river gravels, glacial & lake beds.	Man
			—1 my—		
			Pliocene	Volcanic rocks of Mt. Taylor, early Valle Grande & Gila region; Santa Fe, Gila, and Ogallala Fms.	Mammals
			—11 my—		
			Miocene		
160			—25 my—		
		Paleogene	Oligocene	Datil, Espinaso, and other volcanic rocks.	
			—40 my—		
			Eocene	Baca, Animas, Nacimiento, San Jose, Raton, Poison Canyon, Galisteo, El Rito, Blanco Basin, & Cub Mountain Fms.	
			—60 my—		
			Paleocene		
370	MESOZOIC	Cretaceous		Upper sandstone, shale, & coal. Mesaverde, Pierre, & Niobrara. Dakota Ss. and Mancos Sh.	Dinosaurs
				Volcanic rocks, limestone, sandstone, and conglomerate.	
			—135 my—		
		Jurassic		Morrison Fm., Summerville Fm., Zuni Ss., Todilto Ls. & gypsum, Entrada Ss.	
			—180 my—		
		Triassic		Wingate Ss., Dockum Fm., Chinle Fm., Santa Rosa Ss., Moenkopi Fm.	
	PALEOZOIC	Permian		Rustler Dolomite; redbeds Castile gypsum, Salado Salt.	Amphibians
				Artesia Grp.—Capitan reef San Andres Ls.—Goat Seep reef Glorieta Sandstone Yeso Fm.—Bone Spring Fm.	
				Abo Redbeds—Hueco Ls.	
			—280 my—		
		Pennsylvanian		Mostly limestone; beds of shale & sandstone; lenses of gypsum, salt, and coal.	
			—310 my—		
		Mississippian		Helms & Paradise Fms. Rancheria Ls. Lake Valley & Escabrosa Lss. Arroyo Penasco & Tererro Fms.	Fish
			—345 my—		
		Devonian		Percha Shale, Ouray Ls. northern dol., ss, and sh. erosion	
			—400 my—		
		Silurian		Fusselman Dolomite erosion	
			—425 my—		
1500 +		Ordovician		Montoya Dolomite El Paso Limestone Bliss	Invertebrates
			—500 my—		
		Cambrian		Sandstone erosion	
	PRECAMBRIAN			quartzite, gneiss, rhyolite, andesite, granite, pegmatite, schist, greenstone.	Simple primitive forms

Figure 1. TABLE OF GEOLOGIC TIME

34

plains. But the climate was more humid, and while no large through rivers are known, local great swamps and lakes lay on the plains in debris-trapping lowlands.

Scenery in north-central New Mexico (fig. 2) may have been similar to today's, with mountains in the same general areas as the present-day Sangre de Cristo, Nacimiento, San Juan, and Brazos ranges. Coarse-grained gravels were stacked up at the edges of the mountains, but out in the adjoining lowlands, floodplain sands and varicolored lake-bed clays settled. Three low areas were "basins" of deposition where thick masses of sediments accumulated—the Raton and Poison Canyon formations in the Raton Basin near Raton, the Animas, Nacimiento, and San Jose formations in the San Juan Basin north and northwest of Cuba, seen along

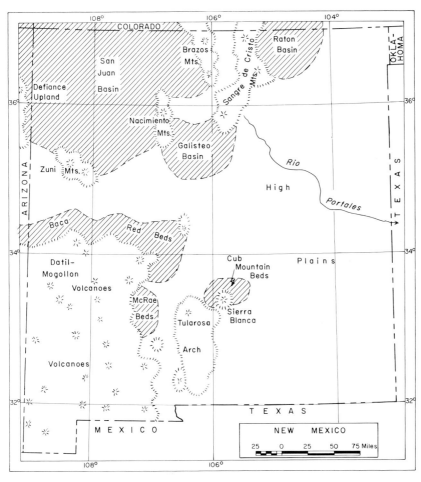

Figure 2. New Mexico during Paleogene time

35

N.M. Highway 44, with thinner deposits of the El Rito and Blanco Basin formations to the northeast of Cuba, and the Galisteo Formation in the Galisteo Basin south and southwest of Santa Fe. Volcanic rocks, the Espinaso beds, overlie the Galisteo but are not much younger in age. Reddish rocks of the Galisteo Formation crop out along U.S. Highway 85 at La Bajada Hill about twenty miles southwest of Santa Fe. The Sandia Mountains' area appears to have been a lowland.

Silicified wood, chiefly of pines but with some oak and poplar, is abundant in the Galisteo Formation. Large logs, up to 6 feet in diameter and 135 feet long, have been found. In the great swamps of the Raton Basin, where the climate was much like that of Georgia today, tall reeds, water lilies, fig trees, palm trees, magnolias, and sycamores grew in profusion, and contributed to the thick coal beds now mined there. The early ages of the Cenozoic saw the spectacular rise of the mammals to dominance over reptiles on land; numerous remains of the early mammals are found in the Nacimiento and San Jose formations, including the famous Puerco and Torrejon faunas—as well as many clams, snails, fish, turtles, crocodiles, snakes, and birds.

Southeastern New Mexico appears to have been relatively level with only local hills and vast regions of featureless, stagnant but high plains where erosion slowly ate downward, deposition was slight, and most of the detritus was carried eastward far beyond the state's borders. The redbeds of the Baca Formation were laid down on the north flank of low mountains that extended intermittently from somewhere near Quemado toward Socorro. Some ancient hills near present-day Sierra Blanca shed rock fragments that accumulated near Capitan as the varicolored Cub Mountain Formation. Deeply eroded uplands northwest of Elephant Butte Reservoir supplied gravels and sands that mingled with andesitic volcanic debris as the upper part of the McRae Formation in central Sierra County. Many of the weathered greenish and purplish volcanic rocks in southwestern New Mexico were extruded at this time, and beneath the surface these molten magmas (hot liquefied rocks) cut into older rocks. Vapors and hot solutions from the magmas are believed to have emplaced some of New Mexico's vast ore deposits during this time.

The last phase of the Paleogene Period, about 25 to 40 m.y. ago, was an earth-shaking time in New Mexico—and the first explosion of an atomic bomb in 1945 on the Jornada del Muerto between Socorro and Carrizozo was a relatively low-energy-yield event compared with the late Paleogene earth movements. Almost the entire southwestern quarter of the state literally exploded, with volcanic eruptions on a grand scale. These lava flows, rock breccias, ashes, pumice, and associated intrusives (molten rocks that did not make it to the surface) form the Datil–Mogollon plateau—at least 100 miles in diameter—as part of the Datil Formation, which locally is miles thick, and made up the main mass of many other ranges near the Mexican border. Sierra Blanca (12,003 feet altitude) northeast of Alamogordo is a huge, isolated volcanic mass of late Paleogene age.

This widespread volcanic activity continued into the Neogene Period which began about 25 m.y. ago. Rhyolites, pumice, and perlite in the southwest, as well as in other parts of the state, covered wide areas. Mount Taylor, towering up to 11,389 feet near Grants and visible on the western skyline from Albuquerque, is a Neogene volcanic pile, as are parts of the Sangre de Cristo range northeast of Taos. Shiprock and Cabezon Peak, landmarks in northwestern New Mexico, are volcanic necks—the eroded cores of ancient volcanoes.

Valle Grande caldera makes up the center of the Jemez Mountains west of Los Alamos and is a late Neogene volcanic mass with the central crater sixteen miles in diameter—one of the world's largest calderas. Bandelier National Monument headquarters is within a canyon carved from Valle Grande's ashes. Volcanic ash scattered over the western parts of Texas, Oklahoma, and Kansas was blown from this volcano. Capulin Mountain, east of Raton, is a huge recent cinder cone and is surrounded by numerous basaltic lava flows that cap the High Plains from Raton eastward to Clayton. The very fresh black basalt flows near Carrizozo and in the valley of Rio San Jose near Grants are probably less than 1000 years old. Numerous mesas along the Rio Grande Valley from the Colorado line to El Paso are capped by black basalt flows of late Neogene age.

Many of the present-day mountains were uplifted in early Neogene time, following the climax of the great volcanic eruptions. This uplifting, in many instances, took place along one side of huge mountain masses, forming tilted fault blocks like the Sandia, Manzano, San Andres, and Sacramento mountains. Rock beds in the Sandia Mountains, for example, dip to the east, but were uplifted along a west-bounding fault zone—a huge break in the earth's crust—as much as four miles! This was an earth-shaking event! However, the uplifting took place slowly, and indeed is continuing today as the Albuquerque area, along with the Rio Grande Valley southward to Socorro, is one of the most active earthquake areas in the state.

Concurrent with uplift, other blocks of the earth's crust sank, forming graben basins which were flooded with rock debris from the adjoining uplifts. A tremendous irregular graben, now followed by the Rio Grande, cut north-south across the state. Geologists label it the *Rio Grande structural depression* (fig. 3). Mountains on the east are the Sangre de

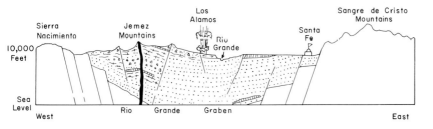

Figure 3. EAST-WEST CROSS SECTION OF RIO GRANDE GRABEN NEAR SANTA FE

Cristo, Sandia, Manzano, Los Pinos, Fra Cristobal, and Caballo ranges; those to the west include the Brazos, Jemez, Ladron, Socorro, Magdalena, and San Mateo mountains. Within this complex graben, and around the bordering ranges, the colorful sandstones and siltstones of the Santa Fe Group were deposited—these red, yellow, orange, and cream rocks are eroded in many places, such as near Santa Fe, to "badlands" characteristic of the landscapes along the Rio Grande Valley from Espanola southward to El Paso. Much brightly tinted silicified wood is found in these beds, and literally freight-car loads of mammalian remains have been shipped to museums from outcrops near Espanola.

In the basins amid the mountains of southwestern New Mexico, similar sands and gravels of the Gila Conglomerate filled low areas. East of the mountains of central New Mexico that form a north-south chain of ranges from Raton to Carlsbad, thin gravels of the Ogallala Formation were dumped onto the western edges of the High Plains. They now cap the plains as well as make picturesque bluffs east of the Pecos River and southeast of Tucumcari—the "caprock" of that area. In northwestern New Mexico, isolated mesas are topped by the Chuska and Bidahochi formations; similar sands, silts, and clays washed from adjoining highlands.

The final episodes of landscape formation occurred during the Pleistocene Epoch, the recent glacial period. Mountain valley glaciers occupied some of the higher parts of the state, as far southward as Sierra Blanca; large lakes filled many of the closed basins, such as those near Estancia and south of Lordsburg; the Carrizozo and Grants basalt flows were extruded; the final tremendous explosions of Valle Grande spread volcanic ash over large regions; sands, gravels, and clays were eroded and deposited by streams and in lakes; and sand dunes were heaped up in many areas. The glistening white gypsum dunes (fig. 4) of White Sands National Monument, built up into 50-foot-high mounds windward of gypsiferous Lake Lucero, are spectacular products of the wind.

The Rio Grande, in its present valley, probably is only as old as mid-Pleistocene, born during late uplift of its headwater mountains, the San Juan and Sangre de Cristo ranges in southern Colorado and northern New Mexico—initiated by floods of meltwaters from waning mountain glaciers. Some of the lower terraces (benches) along the Rio Grande are very young, being dated by radiocarbon methods at 2600 B.P. (before present). Until shackled by Elephant Butte Dam in 1916, and smaller dams up and down the valley, the Rio Grande switched its course with every large springtime flood. Even with these man-made controls, the Rio carves new channels during floods and covers flooded fields with silt as the high waters recede.

PRECAMBRIAN ERA

The highest points in New Mexico are in the north-central region. Here, along the backbone of the Sangre de Cristo Mountains, tower Wheeler Peak (13,160 feet above sea level), northeast of Taos, and South Truchas Peak (13,102 feet), northeast of Santa Fe. Snow lingers on these

Figure 4. GYPSUM DUNES OF WHITE SANDS

lofty spires all year around except during an especially hot August. Highest peaks—they must be capped by the youngest rocks. But no, the quartzites and gneisses, hard rocks made up of quartz and feldspar, that hold up these pinnacles against the attack of water and ice are among the oldest rocks known in the Southwest—perhaps as much as two billion years old. These Precambrian rocks lay deep beneath the earth's surface from early Paleozoic time (500 m.y. ago?) until early Neogene time, then were uplifted along great breaks in the earth's crust, uplifted slowly and intermittently during the span of time from about 20 m.y. ago to perhaps 1 m.y. ago.

How did these ancient rocks form? What did New Mexico look like during the dawn of geologic history? The record in stone is fragmentary. But about two billion or so years back, thick masses of quartz sandstone were laid down in north-central New Mexico, as well as vast lenses of mud, and some beds of feldspar-rich sandstone. Volcanic activity was intense; huge flows of rhyolite and andesite were poured out over most of the state, and these in turn, along with the muddy and sandy sediments, were intruded by enormous masses of hot granite. Mile-high mountains were formed, and during the stretch of this early geologic time, called the Precambian Era, the high peaks were eroded by rain, wind, and sun until some were worn down to featureless plains sloping toward the ancient ancestral oceans.

These Precambian rocks now make up the cores of such mountain ranges as the Sandias east of Albuquerque, the Sangre de Cristo range near Santa Fe, the Pedernal Hills south of Clines Corners, the Burro Mountains southwest of Silver City, the Brazos Range east of Tierra Amarilla, the Zuni Mountains southwest of Grants, and the San Andres Mountains west of White Sands. As seen in Tijeras Canyon east of Albuquerque, the bulk of the ancient rocks are gray to pinkish granite and granite gneiss, speckled by crystals of biotite, microcline, orthoclase, and quartz. Quartzites (hardened sandstones), greenstone, and foliated mica schists (fig. 5) are the older rocks that were intruded by granitic magmas about 1350 million years ago—as indicated by dating of radioactive

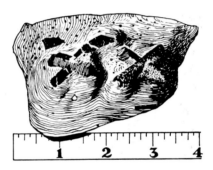

Figure 5. STAUROLITE TWIN CRYSTALS IN MICA SCHIST

isotopes, K-Ar and Rb-Sr. Locally, pegmatite dikes, a late-cooling, large-crystal stage of the granites, crisscross the granite and contain excellent crystals of quartz, feldspar, and mica, as well as less common minerals. The famous Harding pegmatite near Dixon, about forty miles north of Santa Fe, contains beryl, columbite-tantalite, lepidolite mica, spodumene, and other rare minerals. Some of these crystals are ten feet in length!

PALEOZOIC ERA

There are some primitive types of plant and animal life known from Precambrian rocks outside of New Mexico but the earliest beds that contain abundant fossils are those of Cambrian age, 500 to 600 m.y. old. Cambrian rocks in New Mexico are in the Bliss Sandstone, a reddish brown iron-rich bed, 50 to 200 feet thick, that occurs only in the southern part of the state. There it can be seen, for example, along the bold east-facing escarpment of the San Andres Mountains or the west-facing cliffs of the Caballo Mountains, as a dark band resting on the pinkish Precambrian granitic rocks. It is a shallow-sea sand, deposited on the northeastern edge of the Cambrian seas. Scattered amid the brown-stained quartz, red hematite, and green glauconite are broken shells of trilobites and primitive brachiopods. Northern New Mexico was a low, broad island during Cambrian time, a source of some of the sands in the Bliss Sandstone.

During the Ordovician Period, 425 to 500 m.y. ago, upper sands of the Bliss as well as overlying limestones and dolomites were deposited in the shallow warm seas of southern New Mexico; these latter rocks are the El Paso Limestone and Montoya Dolomite. The Ordovician seas teemed with invertebrate life. Fifteen-foot-long cephalopods, as much as a foot in diameter, ruled the shallow salt-water bottoms, munching on the abundant trilobites and the moss animals, the bryozoans. Numerous brachiopods, corals, snails, and clams also thrived, with many of the Ordovician carbonate-rock beds literally being made up of these fossil remains. Near El Paso, these limy fossiliferous beds are nearly 2000 feet thick, but they thin northward to a knife edge in thickness near Mockingbird Gap at the north end of the San Andres Mountains. Parts of northwestern New Mexico may have been low islands exposed to the sun and erosion during Ordovician time, but most of the state was probably within an extensive shallow ocean. Later, erosion removed the Ordovician rocks from central and northern New Mexico.

Silurian strata, the brown Fusselman Dolomite, deposited during the middle of that period (400 to 425 m.y. ago), remain only in the southern and southeastern parts of the state, thinning out northward from the 1000-foot-thick bed near El Paso. The extent of these middle Silurian seas is not known, but most of central and northern New Mexico was undergoing erosion during late Silurian time. The northward thinning of the Fusselman Dolomite is due chiefly to this erosion, evidenced by the knobby, ridged and channeled top surface of the Fusselman. Brachiopods and corals are the most abundant fossils in the Fusselman Dolomite; elsewhere, Silurian rocks are known for the sea scorpions or eurypterids, which attained a length of nine feet, and for the complete remains of primitive fishes.

During early and middle Devonian time (345 to 400 m.y. ago), most of New Mexico was a lowland rotting beneath the sun. Fossiliferous Devonian rocks are unknown in the north-central part of the state but occur beneath the surface in the Four Corners region of northwestern New Mexico and the adjoining states. These rocks are of late Devonian age and consist of lower dolomite and sandstone, middle shale and dolomite, and the upper Ouray Limestone.

In southern New Mexico, a uniform blanket of dark limy muds, called the Percha Shale, was deposited during late Devonian time. This shale marks a great change from the limestones of earlier ages. In part, it is of black muds deposited in widespread or in local stagnant basins and in part calcareous fossiliferous muds in which abundant invertebrate life was buried. The clay and quartz silt that make up the rocks were a weathered residuum that had accumulated, during the long period of late Silurian and early and middle Devonian times, on the lowland of central and northern New Mexico.

Except in the stagnant basins, invertebrate life was prolific, brachiopods, bryozoans, and corals being especially numerous. Fossil fish remnants, chiefly teeth, are abundant in some of the sandy units, and outside of New Mexico the earliest amphibians occur in upper Devonian rocks. The oldest definitely known assemblage of land plants occurs in the Devonian, and forests containing forty-foot-high trees spread over the uplands. Such tree ferns, horsetail rushes, and lycopods (spiked-leafed trees) may have grown in profusion on the swampy lowlands near Albuquerque's and Santa Fe's present sites, far north of the muddy Devonian seas of southern New Mexico.

Mississippian rocks (310 to 345 m.y. old) probably were deposited over most of New Mexico. Subsequent erosion removed much of the Mississippian beds in northern New Mexico. The remnants, less than 100 feet thick in most places, are of lower sandy and shaly beds overlain by massive crinoidal limestones, the Arroyo Penasco Formation of the Nacimiento and Sandia mountains and the Tererro Formation of the Sangre de Cristo range east of Santa Fe.

In southern New Mexico, the Mississippian beds are thick and widespread, being more than 1000 feet in thickness in the southwestern panhandle. There the rock units are the Escabrosa Limestone of the southwest or the Lake Valley Limestone of the south-central part of the state. These are massive fossiliferous limestones precipitated in shallow extensive seas abounding with invertebrate life. Huge gardens of the sea lilies, crinoids, spread over the area, their remains mingled with those of lacy moss animals, the bryozoans, and with brachiopods and corals. Locally, as in the region of the Sacramento and San Andres mountains and Black Range, moundlike fossil reefs, called bioherms, were built. Some of these bioherms in the Sacramento Mountains are mounds of fossiliferous limestones 350 feet high and several thousand feet in diameter. Beds on their flanks dip as much as 35 degrees and are made up of broken "fossil hash" calcite sands. One can stand at the base of these huge limestone hills and almost hear the ancient waves breaking against the reef and see the dying struggle of the brachiopod (fig. 6) that left his shell in the reef-flank sands.

To the south, beginning near the present site of White Sands, dark cherty limestones were laid down in stagnant waters, to become the Rancheria Limestone. This black to reddish brown siliceous limestone is more than 300 feet thick near El Paso. There its thin beds break down into slabs that resemble a jumbled woodpile.

BRACHIOPOD
Marginifera.

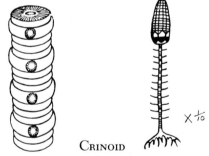

CRINOID
Left, stem fragment; right, restoration of a crinoid.

Figure 6. FOSSIL SPECIMENS

Northern New Mexico was above sea level during late Mississippian time; in some areas caves developed in the porous limestones, and in other places the limestones were eroded to a residuum of chert and red clay. The land must have looked like the karst areas of Indiana, Kentucky, and Illinois today—with lost rivers flowing into sink holes, numerous caves, and many underground rivers. Only the southernmost part of the state was awash in the late Mississippian seas, and in these salt waters, rocks of the Helms and Paradise formations settled. They are typical nearshore beds of yellowish limy sandstone, green limy shales, and brown sandy oolitic limestones. Plant fossils occur intermingled with marine animal remains; the plant fragments were washed into the shallow seas from the land areas of the central and northern parts of the state.

The Pennsylvanian Period (280 to 310 m.y. ago) was a time of change. Previously, northern New Mexico had been an emergent lowland or barely awash in shallow waters, while to the south shallow but extensive seas held sway, the spawning ground of the vertebrates and invertebrates that evolved between 310 and 600 m.y. B.C. But mountains were built during the Pennsylvanian, and the whole pattern of land and sea was altered. The sun rose on north-south aligned ranges interspersed with north-south-trending seas (fig. 7). Somewhere north of Albuquerque a mighty range of mountains, the Uncompahgre Range, arose to shed rock debris into adjoining ocean basins. To the southeast, a lower but prominent range, the Pedernal Mountains, stretched from the present-day Pedernal Hills southward to somewhere near Ruidoso and Piñon. Rocks eroded from this landmass were dumped westward into the Orogrande basin which occupied the region near the present-day White Sands; there as much as 3000 feet of beds accumulated—impure sandstones, dark shales, fragmental limestones, and even some gypsum during the end phase of Pennsylvanian sedimentation.

Rocks filled the Delaware basin in southeastern New Mexico—limestones, sandstones, and black shales that now produce oil and gas. In northwestern New Mexico west of Grants and mostly west of the Zuni Mountains, a low land area, the Zuni Islands, was the source of eroded residuum released into an ocean channelway that ran north-northwest through central New Mexico from El Paso to Farmington. And in the northeast, granite hills of the Sierra Grande Arch stood above the shallow Pennsylvanian seas.

In the Four Corners region, broken rock from the Uncompahgre Range was rushed westward into the Pennsylvanian-age Paradox Basin. Amid the clastic limestones, black shale, gypsum, and salt of this basin are oil-bearing lenses. Today, oil wells pump this black "gold" from the ancient rocks—wells almost in the shadow of Shiprock's famous spire.

The Pennsylvanian Period was a time of coal making on the greatest scale in the earth's history. Extensive swamps and marshes, the habitat of peat and ultimately coal, were almost lacking in New Mexico. Thus, only thin scattered lenses of coal occur in the Pennsylvanian beds of the state. The lands of this period were covered by tree ferns, scale trees, horsetail

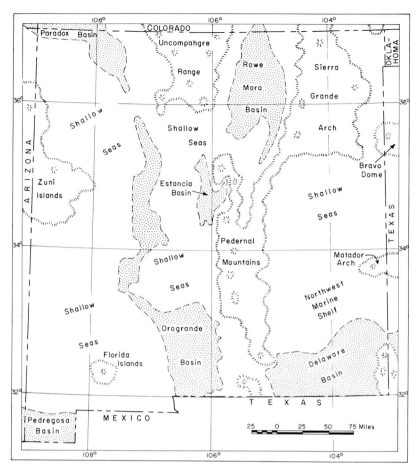

Figure 7. NEW MEXICO DURING PENNSYLVANIAN TIME

rushes, and primitive conifers. In the shallow seas, the dominant invertebrates were fusulinids (fig. 8), small-shelled protozoans shaped like grains of wheat. Abundant cockroaches, large dragonflies, and spiders swarmed over the land.

PERMIAN ROCKS

The Permian Period (230 to 280 m.y. ago) dawned with renewed rising of the highlands in northern New Mexico and southern Colorado. Floods of red sand and clay, washed from the rotting hills, wiped out the seas of northern and central New Mexico, and intertongued southward with marine limestones. These early Permian rocks are the Hueco Limestone near El Paso, there 2200 feet thick, the Abo Redbeds near Albu-

44

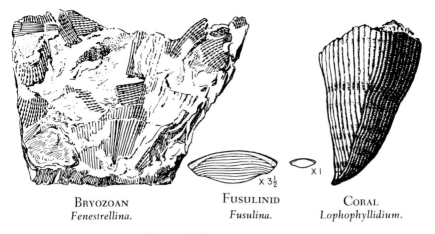

BRYOZOAN
Fenestrellina.

FUSULINID
Fusulina.

CORAL
Lophophyllidium.

Figure 8. FOSSIL SPECIMENS

querque, and the upper Sangre de Cristo Redbeds southeast of Santa Fe. Wherever the redbeds crop out, their dark reddish brown hue, speckled and striped with spots and streaks of green, enlivens the drab gray-and-brown landscape. Some of the reddish coloring is from angular grains of red to orange feldspar, but most is in thin brilliantly tinted skins of hematite that coat the sand grains and saturate the clays. In northern and central New Mexico, amphibians and other primitive vertebrate animals lived amid the red soils and sands; their bones and imprints have been preserved on thin flat slabs of sandstone that now decorate sidewalks and patios.

The early Permian seashore, where limy muds beyond the surf intermingled with red sandy muds swept from the north, vacillated somewhere north of Alamogordo with each sea-level change. Amid the breakers, and as submarine banks in the shallow waters, reefs grew—moundlike masses of shell debris and calcite mud trapped among frondlike calcareous algae. Near Tularosa, these algal "bioherms" are sixty feet high and extend within broad belts half a mile wide. In southeastern New Mexico, these buried "Abo" reefs have yielded much oil.

By the middle of Permian time, the southern Colorado mountains had been worn down to low hills that lay north of an extensive sea covering most of New Mexico. From Santa Fe south to White Sands and southeastward almost to Carlsbad, very shallow marine waters were alternately stifled by pale-red sandy muds or evaporated by the sun. The results were alternating beds of pale-red sandstone, gypsum, and silty dolomitic limestone, called the Yeso Formation. Locally, as near Carrizozo, thick deposits of rock salt also were precipitated, and the Yeso there is about 4000 feet thick. At this time, the Delaware basin of southeastern New Mexico saw the beginning of its most spectacular events, the building of the Capitan and Goat Seep reefs. This basin—a huge oval south of Carlsbad and east of Carlsbad Caverns—had been "deep" sea during most of Pennsylvanian time, but it was a more distinct geographic feature during the Permian. While the pale-red sands, gypsum, halite, and dolomitic limestones of the

45

Yeso Formation were laid down to the north and northwest, the Delaware basin was rimmed by a low, broad bank of fossil-hash calcite sand, now called the Victorio Peak Limestone. In the basin, in deep stagnant waters, black sandy limestone and black shale of the Bone Spring Formation were deposited.

A sheet of white quartz sand filled the late Yeso seas; the resulting Glorieta Sandstone, about 200 feet thick, prominently caps Glorieta Mesa. Its cliffs are a familiar sight to travelers on the Santa Fe Railway at Glorieta Pass. The Coconino Sandstone in the Grand Canyon area of Arizona is the western part of the Glorieta. This "clean" sand—lacking intermixed mud—marks the continued lowering of the southern Colorado uplands. Broad seas then spread over all but northern New Mexico and a thick (600 to 1000 feet) persistent marine unit, the San Andres Limestone, was laid down. Much oil is produced in southeastern New Mexico from this dark-gray unit of limestones and dolomites. The rich agricultural region stretching from Roswell to Artesia depends on underground water gained from the San Andres Limestone, water that falls as rain and snow on the Sacramento Mountains, seeps underground into the cracks and caverns within the San Andres, and flows eastward downslope to the Pecos Valley.

The delicate balance between land and sea swung upward at the end of San Andres time as these late Permian seas retreated to southern New Mexico. The deep Delaware basin was the only persistent marine body of water. It was rimmed by magnificent towering barrier reefs, the Goat Seep and Capitan reefs that now are host to Carlsbad Caverns. These reefs were similar to the present-day Great Barrier Reef of Australia, except that the Capitan and Goat Seep reefs surrounded an inland sea whereas the Australian reef borders a continent. The Capitan reef is about 400 miles long, and other than oceanward channels cut through to the south, completely encircled the 10,000-square-mile Delaware basin. At its heyday, the Capitan reef was barely awash, and teeming with life, in contrast to the silent, stagnant deeps of the Delaware basin which were about 2000 feet below sea level only a few miles away from the barrier reef. On the steep slope into the basin, huge slump blocks of fossiliferous reef limestone slid, mingling with fossil-hash sand. These "flank" beds dip steeply from the massive reef core to interfinger with the black sandy limestones of the basin.

The Delaware basin was a marine feature throughout Late Paleozoic time; its northwestern border is now marked by the southeast-trending front of the Guadalupe Mountains southeast of Carlsbad; its north edge was east-northeast of Carlsbad, and it extended southward into West Texas.

Shallow "shelf" seas reached irregularly and intermittently northward and northwestward from the Capitan reef and mingled with low islands throughout all but southeastern New Mexico. Landward, away from the Delaware basin, the rocks change from massive, thick, light-gray limestones of the reefs into thin units of thin-bedded dolomite, then abruptly into alternating beds of gypsum and redbeds, the Artesia Group of rocks, and finally, marking the distant shorelines, into thin units of red mudstone and red sandstone, the Bernal Formation. Evaporation of sea water was excessive, and average temperatures high; the climate varied from semiarid in northwestern New Mexico to subtropical in the Delaware basin area—a contrast and a similarity to today's climate.

Latest Permian time saw the dramatic end of the Paleozoic Era. Most of New Mexico was uplifted above sea level, with only the Delaware basin remaining as a land-locked sea, much like the Caspian Sea today, but with channels open periodically southward to the ocean. The rocks of this waning part of the Permian are called the *Ochoan Series;* they show an abrupt and striking change from the underlying Carlsbad reef limestones and associated black basin-filling limestones up into the laminated gypsum-anhydrite of the basal Ochoan rocks, the Castile formation. Normal marine conditions ended almost instantaneously. Excess of evaporation lowered the water level of the inland sea; the accumulated brine (concentrated salty sea water) killed the life on and near the Capitan reef, and thick beds of anhydrite were precipitated. The lowest beds of the Ochoan Series, the Castile Anhydrite, and the overlying Salado Salt, mostly filled the deep depression that was the Delaware basin; the upper beds, the Rustler Dolomite and Dewey Lake Redbeds, lap over the edges of the basin and in places rest irregularly upon the Capitan limestone.

These are unusual rocks. The Castile (about 1800 feet thick) is thinly banded, with thicker bands (laminae, thin layers) of light-gray gypsum-anhydrite alternating with thin laminae of dark-brown calcite (fig. 9). This lamination is believed due to annual changes, the brown calcite being precipitated during the summer and the gray anhydrite during the win-

Figure 9. CASTILE GYPSUM SAMPLE

47

ter. On the surface, the calcium sulfate mineral is gypsum, but at depths of about 600 feet, these laminae are anhydrite. Addition of water to anhydrite has changed it to gypsum wherever ground water penetrated the laminae.

The Salado Salt, about 2000 feet thick, is almost entirely of rock salt (halite), with important interbeds of potassium-rich minerals—red sylvite, gray langbeinite, brownish bitter-tasting carnallite, and pale-red polyhalite. As all these salts are highly soluble in water, the Salado Salt nowhere "crops out" at the surface. East of Carlsbad, however, the potash-rich beds are mined underground, and supply about ninety per cent of the United States' production—used chiefly as fertilizer.

The arid period of Salado Salt evaporation changed slightly as the dolomites and anhydrites of the Rustler Dolomite were laid down in the last drying moments (geologically speaking) of the Permian. Then as the seas retreated to the south, the fine-grained red sands and silts of the Dewey Lake Redbeds were spread as a thin blanket over the low lands basking under the hot Permian sun. This was a time of dying; whole races of vertebrate and invertebrate animals were wiped out, to be known today only from their fossil remains. As the dim unmarked episode of latest Permian time merged into the Triassic, an inkling of coming life was recorded in the rocks. The amphibians were more modern types, and they gave rise to the most striking of early land animals, the reptiles. This was the beginning of the conquest of the land by the reptiles, which culminated later in the dinosaurs, and was aided by the retreat of shallow seas from the continents, a change survived chiefly by the species adapted to living on land.

MESOZOIC ERA

The Mesozoic Era dawned in New Mexico on extensive plains, except for a northwest-trending range in the extreme north-central part of the state. During this, the early part of the Triassic Period (180 to 230 m.y. ago), sands and muds eroded from New Mexico were carried westward to northeastern Arizona where they now form the Moenkopi Formation, the brilliant reds and purples of the Painted Desert region. Uplands arose in late Triassic time in southwestern New Mexico. Along with mountains in south-central Colorado, these highlands were torn apart by water and wind, and the detritus was swept into sheets of brightly colored sand and shale. These beds are thickest (about 2000 feet) along the New Mexico–Texas line east of Roswell and in west-central New Mexico (near Grants) extending westward into northeastern Arizona. The eastern Triassic rocks are the redbeds of the Dockum Group with the lower Santa Rosa Sandstone and the upper Chinle beds. The northwestern rocks are the Chinle Formation overlain by the redbeds of the Wingate Sandstone.

The Chinle Formation is of special scenic interest as its beds contain the silicified trees so well shown at Petrified Forest National Monument. These varicolored rocks—red, purple, green, and gray—also decorate the Painted Desert area, the wide valley of Rio San Jose east of Laguna, and flank Interstate 40 (U.S. Highway 66) from the Texas line westward al-

48

most to Clines Corners. As some beds are weathered "ash" beds, the highlands were sites of volcanoes that spread their dust over much of the Southwest. In contrast to the underlying marine Paleozoic rocks, these Triassic beds were deposited on land by streams and in shallow lakes. Thus the beasts that roamed New Mexico were amphibians—such as the thick-skulled stegocephalians—and reptiles of the crocodilelike clan, the phytosaurs. The silicified trees in the Chinle are mostly primitive pines; some grew to heights of more than 100 feet and measure 7 feet in diameter.

New Mexico was featureless rolling prairie, with scattered low hills in the northwest, during most of Jurassic time (135 to 180 m.y. ago). In the late part of the period, the Sundance–Curtis sea and its shoreline lagoons spread down from the north into northwestern New Mexico. Sand dunes on its southeastern shores consolidated into the cross-bedded Entrada Sandstone; its reddish brown cliffs rim the Rio San Jose Valley near Grants and Gallup. In an extensive lagoon, or salt-water lake that covered most of northwestern and north-central New Mexico, the gypsum and limestone of the Todilto Formation were precipitated; this gypsum is the bed mined near Rosario siding (seen between Albuquerque and Santa Fe) by the Kaiser Gypsum Company, and near San Ysidro on White Mesa by the American Gypsum Company. The Todilto salty basin was overwhelmed by reddish sands and silts of the Summerville Formation, washed chiefly from the south, and by the multicolored sands of the Zuni Sandstone (exposed at El Morro), and then the stream and wind-blown sands and clays of the varicolored Morrison Formation were laid down in northern New Mexico. Petrified wood and bone fragments are abundant in the Morrison beds—along with uranium—but no fossil finds in New Mexico equal those in the Morrison Formation of Dinosaur National Park, Utah.

Much of North America, including southern New Mexico, was land during the Jurassic. In the streams and lakes were many kinds of fishes, amphibians, reptiles, snails, crustaceans, and water bugs; on dry land were hordes of reptiles, small primitive mammals, and ants; in the air were flying reptiles, the earliest known birds, moths, and butterflies. The earth was ruled by the reptiles, with the dinosaurs dominant—some being the most ponderous land animals of all earth history. Such were Stegosaurus and Brachiosaurus, the latter 85 feet long and weighing 50 tons.

The Cretaceous Period (70 to 135 m.y. ago) was one of great contrast in New Mexico. During Early Cretaceous time, most of the central and northern parts of the state were low lands torn by erosion, while thick piles of conglomerate, sandstone, and shale accumulated in depressions in the southwestern corner. Huge volcanoes near Lordsburg added their hot ashes, bombs, and flows to the sedimentary detritus, and thick fossiliferous limestones were laid down in muddy and sandy waters of the sea—the shoreline fluctuated over tens of miles in areas south of Lordsburg, Deming, and El Paso. These Early Cretaceous beds total 20,000 feet in thickness in some areas. In eastern and northeastern New Mexico, in contrast, thin

49

sheets of quartz sand were deposited by streams on the edge of a shallow sea, and black muds in local lagoons.

Rock beds thousands of feet thick were laid down in northern and central New Mexico during Late Cretaceous time, whereas most of the southern part of the state was above sea level and was being eroded by tireless winds and streams. The shorelines made parallel northwest-trending bands across the state. These are now marked by beach sands, some of which are speckled by black minerals, high in rare elements titanium, niobium, and zirconium. Northwestern and central New Mexico was a battleground of the land and sea, with the beaches advancing and retreating fifty or a hundred miles during an instant of geologic time. Stream sands and coal beds lie landward from the beach sands which, in turn, mingle seaward with black limy shales that were flushed into the seas. The lowest of these rocks is the Dakota Sandstone—famous as an artesian aquifer in the High Plains areas of states to the northeast—Colorado, the Dakotas, Nebraska, Kansas, Wyoming, and Montana. Above is the black Mancos Shale, which in turn is overlain by the Mesaverde Group.

The transitions from coal swamps and stream sands to beach deposits and then into marine black shales is characteristic of the Mesaverde in northwestern and north-central New Mexico. To the northeast, beds of the same age were laid down in an extensive muddy sea that stretched far to the east; the Pierre Shale and Niobrara chalky limestone that underlie the plains northeast of Las Vegas are typical. The cliff-forming sandstones and coal beds near Gallup are part of the Mesaverde Group and rim the entire San Juan Basin. Above are similar rocks such as the Kirtland Shale, Pictured Cliffs Sandstone, and Fruitland Formation that underlie valleys cut in the shales and cliffs carved from the sandstones in the northwest corner of New Mexico near Farmington.

Toward the end of the Cretaceous, the Laramide "revolution" began, and New Mexico along with most of North America emerged from beneath the seas, to be high and dry to the present. The revolution, an extensive upheaval of the earth's crust, saw uplift of the San Juan Mountains area in southwestern Colorado and large volcanoes spouting fire and ashes nearby. Fragments of the eroded mountains and debris from these andesitic volcanoes were flushed southward by streams and steam to settle as thick piles of mud, sandstone, and conglomerate, the McDermott and Animas formations in the San Juan Basin. The last moment of Cretaceous time, if we could be so precise, was ushered out almost unnoticed— with mountains rising to the north and the andesitic-quartz detritus being laid down to the south in the upper beds of the Animas Formation.

Similarly, mountains arose during Late Cretaceous time in north-central New Mexico and south-central Colorado, about on the site of the present-day Sangre de Cristo range northeast of Taos, and shed erosional gravels and muds into the Raton Basin area. Alluvial fan gravels and sands grade eastward into dark muds and coals laid down in swamps and on floodplains. These rocks now cap the rugged mesas seen northwest of the Santa Fe Railway from Raton southward—the cliff-forming Trinidad Sandstone and the dark siltstones, sandstones, black shales, and coal beds of the Vermejo and Raton formations. The Kaiser Steel Corporation mine near Koehler extracts coal from these beds. Again, the exact end of the Cretaceous is marked only by some obscure boundary between beds, in that area within the Raton Formation.

During the Cretaceous Period, the deciduous trees—such as the oak, maple, poplar, and elm that dominate today's flora—became common. The covered-seed plants, the angiosperms, are the most notable of the Cretaceous plants, but the development of the modern floras was an antecedent to the great expansion of mammals and birds during the following Cenozoic Era. Reptiles ruled the earth, led by the dinosaurs (fig. 10) and their distinctive group, the horned large-skulled ceratopsians such as Triceratops. The small, hairy, warm-blooded mammals were still insignificant creatures that ran from their huge dinosaur lords, but they ate reptile eggs, and so excelled the sluggish reptiles in mental and physical activity that they adapted swiftly to the changing environments of the Laramide revolution —and became dominant as the pea-brained reptiles were unable to stand the changes.

The shallow seas of the Cretaceous swarmed with invertebrate life; foraminifers (unicellular protozoans) in uncountable billions make up large parts of the chalky limestones. Mollusks, particularly clams like oysters and the heavy ribbed Inoceramus, and complexly sutured cephalopods, the ammonites, as well as the internal-shelled belemnoids (that look like cigars), were most numerous among larger marine animals. Reef builders in southwestern New Mexico were the peculiarly corallike clams, the rudistids. Widespread warm humid climates seem to have prevailed throughout the state during most of the Cretaceous.

LANDSCAPES AND MINERAL RESOURCES

Thus as the Cretaceous seas withdrew from New Mexico, the Cenozoic Era dawned, and never again have marine waters shaped the landscapes. The rocks, Precambrian, Paleozoic, Mesozoic, and Cenozoic, and their ancient movements determine New Mexico's spectacular landscapes. They tell tales of the endless war between erosion and hard rock, show the deposition of sediments, their uplift, and their eventual destruction. The result is striking scenery—volcanic mountains, as Mount Taylor, Sierra Blanca, Valle Grande—fresh lava flows near Carrizozo and Grants—volcanic necks like Shiprock and Cabezon—White Sands, the work of the wind— El Morro, Enchanted Mesa, Acoma, and badlands near Santa Fe, the result of weathering and erosion—great fault-line escarpments of the Sandia, Manzano, San Andres, and Sacramento mountains—the work of underground waters at Carlsbad Caverns. And man adds his erosive powers— the huge open-pit copper mine at Santa Rita and countless excavations for rock to build homes, to straighten highways.

The sun can be harsh and hot, the rain sparse, the winter nights fierce cold. But within the rocks are natural resources undreamed of by the early

Figure 10. MAKE WAY FOR 'IS LORDSHIP, THE DINOSAUR!

Indians, almost untouched by the Spanish, and with potential beyond vision for the future. Water, being scarce, is one of the more important resources. With an average yearly precipitation of only fifteen inches, and more than half of the state receiving less than that average, water is a problem! Farming must depend upon irrigation, the water being drawn from streams or "mined" from underground "pools" where it had been accumulating for centuries.

Forests, game, and fish are lucrative resources somewhat unexpected in a semiarid state; sheep and cattle—in this the stronghold of the cowboy, famous in gunfighter lore—each total more than a million. New Mexico's 1965 mineral production, valued at $781.9 million, ranked seventh among the states. Principal commodities won from the rocks, in order of value, were oil, potash, natural gas, uranium, copper, sand and gravel, zinc, coal, crushed stone, and perlite. Sizeable quantities of barite, beryl, carbon dioxide, cement, clays, gem stones, gold, gypsum, helium, iron ore, lead, limestone, magnesium compounds, manganese, mica, molybdenum, pumice, salt, silver, sulfur, and vanadium were also mined. The huge open-pit copper mine at Santa Rita, the many uranium mines near Grants, the underground potash mines near Carlsbad, and the thousands of oil and gas wells in the northwestern and southeastern parts of the state are typical of man-made landscape features attributable to mineral exploitation in New Mexico. Numerous old mine dumps, rotting mine shafts, and spooky ghost towns are reminders of past fortunes won and lost.

The rocks, the work of water, wind, and sun, and the not insignificant upheavals by man have shaped New Mexico's landscapes. Blended with its blue skies, warm sun, and the products of three cultures—Indian, Spanish, and American—the rocks and their movements have made the landscapes a land of enchantment.

> Earth wears a mantle rich with lore,
>   of storied fabric finely spun,
> That tells of kingdoms come and gone,
>   of legions lost and battles won.
> No seer no monarch can divine,
>   the cryptic writings; he alone,
> Who humbly speaks the tongue of earth,
>   can find a story in a stone.

Before Coronado

by Robert H. Weber

The cultural heritage of New Mexico is a rich and colorful one, blending as it does the three separate traditions of Indian, Spanish, and Anglo–American. Of these, the lifeways of the Indian, ancient and modern, are of particular interest to both the visitor and resident. These were the first inhabitants of the New World, whose roots extend back in time many thousands of years before the first European set foot here. People who had adapted themselves to the varied and often harsh environments of desert, plain, valley, canyon, and mountain; who witnessed the disappearance of the large mammals of the Pleistocene Ice Age and concomitant changes in climate and vegetation; the first prospectors and miners seeking flint, obsidian, turquoise, clay, salt, and mineral pigments; early traders exchanging valued minerals and handicrafts for shells of the coastal regions; hunters and farmers, architects and builders, civic and religious leaders, philosophers and critics, skilled craftsmen and artists, explorers and soldiers —all ancient counterparts of those who were to follow.

In 1540, when the train of soldiers in the company of Coronado's Spanish Expedition entered the unknown lands later called New Mexico, four groups of native Americans were established residents in the area. Along the arable valley of the Rio Grande and its tributaries, and in several outlying areas were the adobe and stone apartment-house villages of the Pueblo Indians, whose livelihood was based largely on agriculture. East of the mountains were scattered bands of Plains Indians, Eastern Apaches, who were nomadic hunters following the herds of buffalo that ranged across the vast grasslands of the High Plains. Western Apaches were dispersed in small bands of hunters and gatherers of wild foods through the mountainous country to the west of the Rio Grande. A related group, the Navajo, augmented the necessities of life gained by hunting and gathering with subordinate agricultural crops in the Plateau region to the northwest.

Early contacts of the *conquistadores* were largely with the Pueblo Indians, although they had limited knowledge of the Apaches and Navajos in outlying districts. There was little to suggest to the Spanish invaders, except for the ruins of long-abandoned Pueblo villages, that the fragmentary record of thousands of years of human prehistory lay scattered in the dust beneath their feet. Undoubtedly they would have dismissed as utter nonsense any notion that men armed with stone-tipped spears had here slain elephants in a marsh 12,000 years old that now lay buried beneath shifting sands of a desert landscape. Indeed, it was not until the last quarter of the 1800's that serious attempts were made to decipher the prehistoric traces of the Pueblo Indians, whereas concrete evidence that man had hunted long-extinct Pleistocene big game in America was not discovered until less than forty years ago.

EARLY HUNTERS

The year 1926 was marked by the first of a series of important archeological finds in New Mexico that were eventually to demonstrate that man had occupied this area as much as 11,000 to 12,000 years ago. During this period, Late Pleistocene ice sheets of continental glaciers still blanketed parts of the northern tier of states in the vicinity of the Great Lakes, and elephants (both mammoths and mastodons), horses, camels, giant bison, tapirs, and ground sloths roamed the Southwest. Excavations begun in 1926 near the small town of Folsom, in northeastern New Mexico (fig. 1), disclosed a number of fossil skeletons of a large form of extinct bison, forerunners of the modern bison or buffalo. Among these bones were dart or spear points of distinctive form and workmanship, characterized by broad, shallow flutes or channels on each face (fig. 2). These artifacts, now known as Folsom points, have since been recovered from a number of sites in New Mexico and elsewhere in North America, commonly in association with the remains of extinct bison. Evidently Folsom "Man" (whose skeletal remains have not been discovered) was a nomadic hunter particularly dependent upon the bison for his food supply, much as were the later Plains Indians of historic time. Ages of from 10,000 to 11,000 years have been obtained from charcoal and other organic remains at Folsom camp sites by the radiocarbon method.

Succeeding years have seen an increasing number of valuable archeological discoveries at camp and game-kill sites of Folsom Man and other Early Hunters. Unquestionably, the most important of these sites is the Blackwater Draw locality between Clovis and Portales in extreme eastern New Mexico, where excavations for gravel disclosed a stratified sequence of sediments that were deposited in an ancient pond and spring. Here, too, were the characteristic Folsom points in association with the bones of fossil bison. Below the Folsom layer, still older deposits contained the fossil bones of mammoth, horse, camel, and bison associated with fluted spear points that resembled those from Folsom but were generally larger and less skillfully chipped and fluted. These points, now known as Clovis points, are so commonly found beside the remains of mammoths in a number of sites in the High Plains and the Southwest that their makers are believed to have been adept at hunting these extinct elephants. Radiocarbon dates place Clovis points in a time range of from 11,000 to 12,000 years ago.

In a layer above that containing Folsom points at Blackwater Draw, several varieties of unfluted lanceolate points were found to be associated with the bones of fossil bison. These points have been identified by various specific names such as Plainview, Milnesand, Eden, and Scottsbluff from excavated sites elsewhere in the High Plains region, and probably range in age from 8000 to 10,000 years. Although the giant bison still survived into this level of stratigraphy and time, the elephant, camel, and horse of the Clovis level had disappeared from the area.

Another important discovery was made in Sandia Cave northeast of

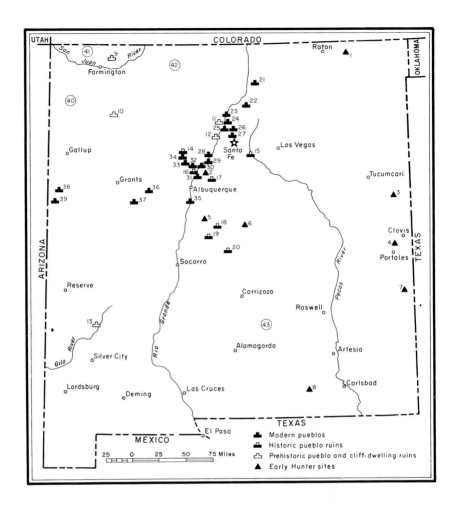

Figure 1. INDEX MAP OF NEW MEXICO SHOWING LOCATIONS OF SIGNIFICANT
ARCHEOLOGICAL SITES, MODERN INDIAN PUEBLOS, AND NAVAJO, UTE, AND
APACHE RESERVATIONS

Early Hunter Sites
1. Folsom State Monument
2. Sandia Cave
3. San Jon
4. Blackwater Draw
5. Manzano Cave
6. Lucy
7. Milnesand
8. Burnet Cave

Prehistoric Pueblo and Cliff-Dwelling
Ruins
9. Aztec Ruins National Monument

10. Chaco Canyon National
    Monument
11. Puye Cliff Dwellings
12. Bandelier National Monument
    (Tyuonyi)
13. Gila Cliff Dwellings National
    Monument

Historic Pueblo Ruins
14. Jemez State Monument
15. Pecos State Monument
16. Coronado State Monument
    (Kuaua)

56

Albuquerque. Below cave deposits containing Folsom points was an earlier type of point among the bones of mammoth, horse, camel, and other large Pleistocene mammals. Now identified as Sandia points, these projectile tips are distinguished by an asymmetric stemmed form with a shoulder on one side. The age of the Sandia points has been a subject of some controversy, but the latest available data from charcoal in Sandia Cave indicates an age of nearly 12,000 years, which is within the accepted range of the Clovis points.

Clovis, Sandia, and Folsom points, together with related stone implements, are at many places enclosed in sediments deposited in or adjacent to ponds, lakes, streams, and wet meadows. These environments indicate

Figure 2. FOLSOM POINT RECOVERED FROM AMONG RIB BONES OF FOSSIL BISON AT FOLSOM, NEW MEXICO
(Photograph of plastic replica. Original point in collection of Denver Museum of Natural History.)

a former cool and more humid climate in areas that are now semiarid. The food requirements of many of the large herbivores that lived at this time also suggest more abundant vegetation and surface water than prevails here today. It is not unreasonable, then, to presume that climatic conditions contributing to the advance of continental glaciers in the Great Lakes region, and to valley glaciers in the Rocky Mountains, should have been reflected in lower summer temperatures and higher rainfall in non-glaciated areas. The ultimate extinction of the large Pleistocene mammals and the similar time of disappearance of the hunters who preyed upon them may both be related to the climatic changes that followed the end of the Ice Age in America.

HUNTERS AND GATHERERS

Groups of people dependent upon a different way of life from that of the Early Hunters are known to have occupied much of the present area of New Mexico. Although there is some suggestion of overlap in time of these people with the Early Hunters, they appear to have become prominent during the several thousand warm, dry years following the end of the Pleistocene. Adapted, as they were, to a fuller utilization of the resources of the area through the hunting and trapping of smaller game and an emphasis on the gathering of a wide variety of wild plant foods, these people ranged extensively across the varied terrain of the state. Similar patterns of subsistence and artifacts are known from the Great Basin region west of the Rocky Mountains, where they have been categorized under the term *Desert Culture*. Local manifestations of the Desert Culture in southeastern Arizona, extending eastward into western and southern New Mexico, are identified as the Cochise Culture. Other groups showing similarities with Archaic cultures to the east penetrated the northeastern part of New Mexico at a time when the area was still populated by Pleistocene bison.

Habitation sites of these gatherers are distributed in open situations and in shelter caves. Such sites are commonly marked by milling stones that characterize the preparation of wild foods (fig. 3), hearths, chopping and scraping implements, and stemmed projectile points markedly different from those used by the Early Hunters. These points were affixed to dart shafts that were propelled with a spear thrower or *atlatl,* a device that preceded the bow and arrow in America but is still used by Australian Aborigines.

Seasonal changes in the local availability of wild foods must have necessitated a nomadic or seminomadic way of life. The development of agricultural techniques in the later years before the beginning of the Christian Era, however, probably contributed to the development of a semisedentary existence that was eventually to lead to the village life of the later periods. The exact time of introduction of the principal agricultural crops, corn, squash, and beans, is unknown, but evidence from west-central New Mexico indicates their use by the Cochise people by 2500 B.C.

PUEBLOAN FARMERS

Having acquired the techniques of deliberately planting and raising food crops that could be stored against future needs, local populations of Hunters and Gatherers became less dependent upon the gathering of

Figure 3. MILLING STONES OF THE TYPE USED BY THE COCHISE PEOPLE
Plant foods were ground in a shallow basin metate with the small one-hand mano
(hand stone). Socorro, New Mexico.

wild foods and began to construct clusters of more permanent dwellings
near cultivable land. Among the earliest recognized houses of this period
are the semisubterranean pit houses of the early Mogollon people in the
San Francisco River drainage of west-central New Mexico (fig. 4) and
of the Anasazi Basketmakers in the San Juan River drainage of northwestern New Mexico. These cultural advances, together with the ac-
quisition of techniques for the manufacture of fired pottery, foreshadowed
the development of the Mogollon and Pueblo cultures at a time beginning perhaps as early as 300 B.C. for the Mogollon area and at least by 1
A.D. for the Anasazi area.

These two cultural groups, the Mogollon in southwestern and southern
New Mexico, whose roots extend back through the ancestral Cochise to
before 6000 B.C., and the Anasazi in the Four Corners region of northwestern New Mexico, probably developed independently during the early
years. From about 500 A.D., however, there is increasing evidence of trade
relationships and eventual fusion of traits. Other groups to the west, such
as the Hohokam of Arizona, were sources of cultural influence on the
indigenous people of New Mexico. In the Mogollon and San Juan Anasazi
heartlands and in the Rio Grande Valley of central New Mexico, a pattern
of village life with elaboration of social and religious organization emerged
from the relatively simple cultures of the early years. Villages began to
assume organized form, dwellings were combined in rows of adobe and
stone structures containing a number of contiguous rooms, and subterranean ceremonial chambers or *kivas* assumed larger and more specialized
architectural distinctiveness from the ancestral pit-house dwellings. In the
Mogollon area, the characteristic brownware pottery of the Mogollons

59

(*Photograph of museum diorama courtesy of the
Chicago Natural History Museum*)
Figure 4. MOGOLLON PIT-HOUSE VILLAGE OF THE PERIOD 200 B.C.

was used side by side with decorated black-on-white pottery of Anasazi origin. The bow and arrow slowly replaced the less efficient *atlatl* and dart. The significance of these early stages in the evolution of the Pueblo Culture in the San Juan and upper Rio Grande areas is indicated by their designation as the Developmental Pueblo period (Pueblo I and II).

The climax of these developments occurred in the interval between 1050 and 1300 A.D. in the Classic or Great Pueblo period (Pueblo III). Among the most impressive manifestations of this period are large stone-masonry apartment houses, some rising to five stories in height and housing hundreds of people. Dwellings of this type are highlights of several well-known tourist attractions, among which are the cliff dwellings of Mesa Verde in southwestern Colorado and the monumental ruins of Pueblo Bonito in Chaco Canyon (fig. 5), both products of the ingenuity of the Anasazi Indians.

At the very apex of the cultural efflorescence of the Great Pueblo period, some unknown circumstance or series of events caused abandonment of most of the urban centers of the San Juan Anasazi and Mogollon areas. A prolonged drouth is recorded by tree rings formed during the period from 1276 to 1299 A.D. Surely a drouth of this magnitude would have had

60

(Photograph courtesy of the National Park Service)
Figure 5. PUEBLO BONITO, CHACO CANYON NATIONAL MONUMENT
A multistory pueblo containing 800 rooms.

serious effects on people as dependent upon agriculture as were the Pueblo Indians. There are some indications that alien and perhaps enemy people were drifting into these areas at about this time, perhaps predecessors of the modern Navajos and Apaches. The congested living conditions of Pueblo villages undoubtedly contributed to unsanitary conditions and social pressures that also may have contributed to shifts in population. Many of these migrants moved into the homeland of the Rio Grande Anasazi in the upper Rio Grande Valley, and to a lesser extent in the central Rio Grande Valley. Some may have relocated at Zuni and other areas along the Little Colorado River drainage extending westward into Arizona.

During the Great Pueblo period, another group showing characteristics of both the Anasazi and of non-Puebloan people occupied an area on both sides of the Continental Divide along the eastern margin of the San Juan Basin. This cultural phase, known as the Largo–Gallina because of the distribution of sites in the Largo and Gallina drainage basins, is represented by pit houses, surface rooms, and towerlike structures with some similarities to the dwellings of the Anasazi. The black-on-white pottery also suggests Puebloan relationships, whereas the culinary vessels resemble those of the Navajo.

Beginning at about 1300 A.D. or shortly thereafter, a different cultural group began to move westward from the Texas Panhandle into the plains of northeastern New Mexico. These people of the Panhandle Aspect built single-room structures and contiguous room pueblos resembling those in use by the Anasazi of the Rio Grande and were skilled bison hunters, farmers, and traders. This combination of traits suggests both Puebloan and eastern traditions. Panhandle Aspect villages were abandoned suddenly not long after 1400, perhaps as a result of the drouth recorded by tree rings for the period from 1439 to 1454.

Following the shift in population of the Pueblo region, cultural changes occurred that have led to the designation Regressive Pueblo period (Pueblo IV) for the interval between 1300 and 1700 A.D. Noteworthy changes during this period include a tendency toward enlargement of villages and the creation of new styles of pottery, accompanied by some deterioration of the artistic creativity of the Classic period. Major ruins of this period that are readily accessible to the public include Puye Cliff Dwellings, Tyuonyi Pueblo in Bandelier National Monument, and Pecos Pueblo in Pecos National Monument.

At the time of Coronado's *entrada* in 1540, there were from 60 to 70 Pueblo villages in New Mexico, most of which contained fewer than 400 inhabitants. Four or five mutually unintelligible languages were spoken, each with several dialects, making communication between Spanish and Indian extremely difficult. Language barriers contributed to an inadequate documentation of the Pueblo way of life during the early years of Spanish contact, so that we must continue to depend upon the archeological record during the first century of Spanish colonization of the area. The beginning of the Historic Pueblo period (Pueblo V) accordingly is commonly set at 1700 A.D.

APACHES AND NAVAJOS

Little is known concerning the origin of these two related groups, who differ markedly from the Pueblo Indians in language and cultural traits. Their closest ties are with other Athapaskan-speaking tribes in northwestern Canada, and available evidence indicates that they are comparative newcomers to the Southwest. A correlation between the abandonment of sections of the Pueblo region and pressures exerted by ancestral Apaches and Navajos has been suggested, but definite proof of this is still lacking. Raids against the eastern pueblos of the Galisteo Basin are reported to have occurred in 1525. Coronado's expedition encountered nomadic hunters in the plains east of Pecos in 1541, observing that they followed the movements of herds of bison or buffalo on whom they were highly dependent for food and shelter, lived in portable tents of tanned buffalo hides supported by a framework of poles, and used dogs as beasts of burden. Trade contacts with the Rio Grande pueblos included exchange of hide "cloaks" for corn grown by the Pueblo Indians.

Related groups in western and northwestern New Mexico are even more poorly known, as there was still less contact between them and the Spanish explorers. Evidently some agriculture was practiced as a supplement to a subsistence based largely on hunting and gathering, a pattern of livelihood reminiscent of that of the pre-Puebloan Cochise people.

The succeeding years of Spanish and American colonization of New Mexico were to be highly influenced by the Apaches and Navajos, and also by another group of Plains Indians, the Comanches. The events of this period, however, are discussed in a separate article.

Frontier Forts of New Mexico

by Robert A. Bieberman

Following President Polk's declaration of war against Mexico in May 1846, a United States Army force was sent from Ft. Leavenworth, Kansas Territory, against the Mexican provinces of New Mexico and California. This army, known as "The Army of the West," was led by Gen. Stephen W. Kearny. Upon his arrival in Santa Fe in August 1846, General Kearny issued a proclamation which informed the citizens that New Mexico was now a part of the United States and that he and his army and the forces to follow would protect them and their property. General Kearny remained in Santa Fe only one month, but during that month he appointed a governor, judges, and other officials, started construction of a fort in Santa Fe, and sent troops against the Navajo Indians in fulfillment of his promise to protect the people. Kearny and his "Army of the West" left Santa Fe in September 1846 to conquer California, leaving behind a detachment of troops under the command of Col. Alexander W. Doniphan. Thus began the role of the U.S. Army, which was to continue for the next half century, in securing the frontier in what we now know as the State of New Mexico.

History has shown that the troops stationed in New Mexico were called upon to participate in the Mexican War and the Civil War and to protect the newly established border between Mexico and New Mexico from violations from both sides. However, the basic role of the military, the role which continued for fifty years, was to protect the traveler, the farmer, the miner, and the settler from Indian attack. Its task was made no less difficult by the changing, unrealistic, discriminatory Indian policies which came out of Washington during this period. When relative calm was established, promises were forgotten and violence erupted anew.

The defense policy in New Mexico did not follow a set plan but gradually evolved. Military posts were established at different places when the need arose and were abandoned when the need diminished. A few of the posts were occupied and used by the army throughout most of this period. Others existed but a few months or years.

FORTS

Fort Union

Located twenty-seven miles northeast of Las Vegas, Fort Union became the most important and most famous fort in the New Mexico Territory. Established on the Santa Fe Trail in 1851, it served as supply depot for the territory and as a base for troops engaged in the protection of traffic along the Santa Fe Trail and of the settlements in the area from the depredations of the Apaches, Utes, Comanches, and Kiowas. The site can be reached by traveling eight miles of paved road which leaves U.S. Highway 85 one mile north of Watrous.

During its forty-year history, Fort Union occupied three different sites, all within the same general area. The original fort was of log construction which rapidly fell into disrepair. In August 1861, amid rumors of the possible invasion of the territory by Confederate forces, construction was begun on a new fort. This fort was of earthworks, in the form of an eight-pointed star. It was here that the troops waited for the attack which never came. With the passing of the Confederate threat, work was begun in 1863 on the third fort, the remains of which are seen today.

Fort Union soon became the largest fort in the territory. It was constructed in two sections, one for the garrison and one for the supply depot. The garrison area consisted of four infantry and two cavalry barracks facing a row of nine officers' quarters across the parade ground. A sixty-bed hospital was constructed. The depot area included five warehouses, mechanics corral, transportation corral, and administration buildings. An arsenal was built about one mile from the fort proper.

The buildings were constructed of adobe on stone foundations. The roofs were flat and the walls were capped with brick copings in what has become the territorial style of architecture.

(Photo courtesy of National Park Service)

RUINS OF FORT UNION

Fort Union was a community within itself and a lively social center. Weary travelers on the Santa Fe Trail eagerly anticipated their arrival. Few complaints were heard when soldiers were transferred to Fort Union, for this was a popular assignment.

With the coming of the railroad and peace at last descending on the frontier in the 1880's, the need for the fort diminished. But it clung to life for a few more years, mainly because of the fond memories which lived in the hearts of the military leaders who had been stationed there. Finally, the end came and Fort Union was abandoned in February 1891.

New life came to the fort in 1955 when it became a National Monument. The ruins have been excavated and stabilized and a fine visitors' center and museum has been established. Fort Union has at last assumed its rightful place as a shrine of history. Stand on the parade ground and survey the majesty that was Fort Union, listen for the sounds, the bugle calls, the barklike commands of close-order drill, the creak of wagons, and the thunder of horses' hooves. These are the sounds of Fort Union. They are still there if one will only pause and listen.

FORT MARCY

Fort Marcy was established in 1846 at Santa Fe and was named for the then Secretary of War, W. L. Marcy. The fort was located on a hill overlooking the city some 1000 yards northeast of the plaza. A deep ditch or moat surrounded the massive adobe walls of the fort and a blockhouse, within musket range, protected the only entrance. At the time of Colonel Manfield's inspection trip in August 1853, the troops were quartered in public buildings in Santa Fe, there being no quarters provided at the fort; however, it could be occupied on a moment's notice. The original Fort Marcy was abandoned in 1867 and a new one was constructed a short distance to the west. This new site is now occupied by business and residential properties. The War Department abandoned Fort Marcy in October 1894, the troops and equipment being moved to Fort Sill, Oklahoma. The site was turned over to the city of Santa Fe in 1897.

Fort Marcy played an important role during the military occupation of New Mexico. It served as a base of operations against marauding Indians, was captured and occupied for a short time by Confederate forces in 1862, served as headquarters for the Ninth Military Department (changed to Department of New Mexico in 1853) throughout most of this period, and was a center for the social life of Santa Fe. Only low mounds of earth now mark the site of Fort Marcy.

FORT WINGATE

Fort Wingate, at the site known today, was established in 1868. It is located on the site of a pre-existing fort at Ojo del Oso (Bear Springs) about twelve miles east of Gallup and three miles south of U.S. Highway 66.

Fort Fauntleroy was established in August 1860 and was named for the then Department Commander, Col. T. T. Fauntleroy. The name was changed to Fort Lyon in September 1861 after Colonel Fauntleroy resigned his commission and joined the Confederate forces. The fort was abandoned in December 1861 as troops were concentrated at other posts to meet the threat of invasion of the territory by Confederate forces from the south. With the defeat of Confederate troops early in 1862, the military returned to the Indian problem and established a post some sixty miles to the east on the Rio de Gallo near San Rafael. This post was named Fort Wingate in honor of Capt. Benjamin Wingate who died of wounds received during the battle with the Confederate forces at Val Verde. The post proved to be too far from the Navajo country for effective control and, in 1868, was abandoned and a new Fort Wingate established at Ojo del Oso on the site occupied earlier by Fort Fauntleroy.

The physical plant of the new Fort Wingate consisted of barracks, officers' quarters, hospital, guard house, storehouse, employees' quarters, corrals, barns, and various repair and storage sheds, all bordering the traditional rectangular parade ground. Some of these buildings are in use today.

In 1914, 4000 Mexican refugees lived in a tent city at Fort Wingate until peace was restored after Pancho Villa's revolution in Mexico. Following World War I, it became an ordnance storage depot, and new administrative and living quarters were built several miles west of the original fort enclosure. This installation is known today as Fort Wingate Ordnance Depot, and the long rows of concrete ammunition storage bunkers can be seen from U.S. Highway 66. In 1925, the original fort enclosure was transferred to the Department of the Interior for use as an Indian school. Today, the parade ground is a playground and the barracks are dormitories for the children who attend this school. The missile age came to Fort Wingate in 1963 when a portion of the military reservation became the launching site for test rockets which impact at the White Sands Missile Range 200 miles to the south.

Fort Wingate has seen many changes during its long and colorful history. It served well during its first 100 years and continues to serve today.

FORT CRAIG

Fort Craig was established in the spring of 1854 on the abandonment of Fort Conrad, nine miles north. It was named in honor of Col. L. S. Craig who was killed by an army deserter on June 6, 1852. The remains of Fort Craig are located on the west bank of the Rio Grande about thirty-four miles south of Socorro and five miles, by dirt road, east of U.S. Highway 85. The fort was established to afford protection against the many bands of Apaches that roamed this part of the territory.

Fort Craig was well built and became one of the best-garrisoned military posts in New Mexico. Built on the usual rectangular plan, the parade ground was bordered on the northeast by two double officers' quarters; on the northwest by the guard house, prison room, and sallyport; on the southwest by three soldiers' barracks each in the form of a hollow

REMNANTS OF GUARD HOUSE, FORT CRAIG
(built of basalt blocks)

square enclosing a patio; and on the southeast by various workshops, store-rooms, stables, and corrals. The commanding officers' quarters occupied the west corner of the parade ground and the hospital the east corner. Behind the commanding officers' quarters there were three large bombproof store-rooms. The entire installation was enclosed within a high wall, beyond which a ditch encircled the fort. Gun bastions projected from the north and south corners.

Fort Craig was one of the most important military posts in New Mexico. Its troops participated in many engagements with the Indian. In the fall of 1861, troops from other posts were concentrated at Fort Craig to meet the threatened invasion of Confederate forces from the south. In February 1862, these troops were defeated by the Confederate invaders in the battle of Val Verde which took place about four miles north of the fort. Upon the withdrawal of Confederate forces from the territory later in 1862, the troops at Fort Craig returned to the Indian problem. In March 1885, the fort was relinquished by the army and the improvements sold. The last soldier left in August 1885 after all government property was removed and sent to Forts Bliss and Stanton. The buildings were sold at public auction on April 30, 1894, to the Valverde Land and Irrigation Company for $1070.50.

Fort Craig is now a ruin, but the outlines of most of the buildings can still be seen. Portions of the plastered walls of the commanding officers' quarters remain, as do portions of the hospital and stone guard house. The wall and ditch surrounding the fort, gun bastions, storehouses, and cemetery are still much in evidence. Coal marks the blacksmith's shop and broken bottles the sutler's store. Another frontier fort has passed into history.

Fort Stanton

Fort Stanton was established in May 1855 on the Rio Bonito at a site located approximately four miles east of present-day Capitan and three miles south of U.S. Highway 380. The fort was an attempt to control the Mescalero and White Mountain Apaches and was named for Capt. H. W. Stanton who had been killed by Apache Indians earlier that year. Many a soldier stationed at Fort Stanton gave up his life to an Apache during the Indian wars.

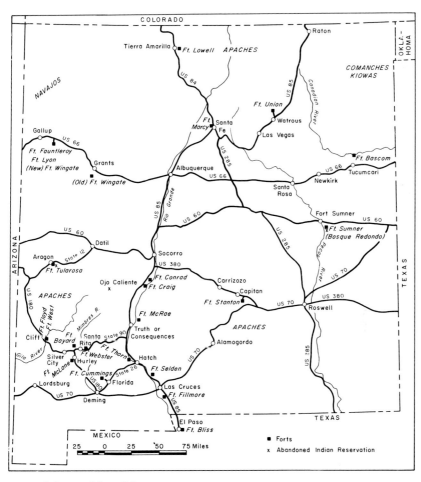

MAP OF NEW MEXICO SHOWING LOCATION OF FRONTIER FORTS

The original fort was little more than a stockade, with few buildings and little equipment. In August 1861, the government stores were burned and the troops moved to Albuquerque in the face of the Confederate invasion. Confederate troops occupied the site one month later but promptly left after a few encounters with the Apache. The site was reoccupied by Union troops October 1862 and, later, substantial buildings were erected, most of which still stand.

With the passing of the frontier, Fort Stanton was abandoned as a military post in August 1896, and in 1899, the installation passed to the U.S. Public Health Service for use as a merchant marine hospital for the treatment of tuberculosis. During World War II, a German prisoner of war camp was established at the fort. In 1953, the hospital was closed by the federal government because of the high cost of running the establishment. Fort Stanton is now a state tuberculosis hospital operated by the New Mexico Department of Public Welfare.

Col. Kit Carson used the fort as a base of operations while rounding up the Mescalero and White Mountain Apaches in late 1862 and early 1863. In 1881, the famous outlaw, Billy the Kid, was confined in the building now used as a dental clinic while on his way to the gallows in Lincoln, which never claimed him. Gen. John J. Pershing, as a young lieutenant, was stationed for a time at Fort Stanton.

Fort Selden

Fort Selden was established in 1865 and named for Capt. Henry R. Selden (later colonel) who distinguished himself at the battle of Val Verde, February 21, 1862. The fort was beside the Rio Grande nine miles north of the settlement of Doña Ana. The site is located along U.S. Highway 85 about seventeen miles north of present-day Las Cruces.

Fort Selden was one of a chain of forts established to control the Apaches. It was on the Butterfield Trail and provided protection for the government rope ferry which crossed the Rio Grande at nearby Leasburg. The summit of Mt. Robledo, across the river to the west, was used as a heliograph station, flashing messages between Fort Selden and Fort Bliss at Franklin (El Paso, Texas).

The buildings of the fort were one-story adobe structures with walls two feet thick. The installation included barracks for enlisted men, two double officers' quarters, a ten-bed hospital, stone guard house, store houses, workshop, bake shop, corrals, and a magazine with stone walls three feet thick. The fort was rectangular in ground plan, the buildings enclosing a parade ground.

Fort Selden was abandoned in 1879 when the railroads began to draw travel away from the overland trails. It was reoccupied in 1881 when the Apache Chiefs Victorio, Nana, and later Geronimo were on the warpath. With the passing of the Indian problem, Fort Selden was permanently abandoned in 1892. During World War I, the grounds of the fort were used for cavalry maneuvers by units stationed at Fort Bliss.

A rather famous American once lived at Fort Selden. Gen. Douglas

MacArthur, as a child of four, moved with his family to the fort in 1884, following the assignment of his father, then an infantry captain, to that post. The family remained at Fort Selden until late in 1886.

Now only crumbling adobe walls mark the site of Fort Selden, once a welcome sight to travelers in southern New Mexico. The wind, rain, and sun have taken their toll, aided in no small way by man himself. In 1963, through the efforts of the Doña Ana Historical Society, Fort Selden was made a State Monument by the New Mexico legislature. It is to be hoped that the fort will now be protected from further weathering and vandalism so that the remnants of this old outpost will stand for many years to come as a monument to the men who once manned it.

Fort Cummings

Fort Cummings was established in October 1863 in what is now Luna County, New Mexico. It was located at Cooke's Spring, an important watering stop on the Butterfield Trail, at the eastern edge of Cooke's Canyon. Prior to the establishment of Fort Cummings, the Apaches made frequent and fatal attacks upon travelers as they passed through the four miles of Cooke's Canyon or stopped at the spring. Cooke's Canyon was one of the most dangerous stretches on the Butterfield Trail. The fort was named for Maj. Joseph Cummings who was killed by Navajo Indians in August 1863. Its ruins can be reached by turning off State Highway 26 at Florida, sixteen miles northeast of Deming, and traveling seven miles to the west.

Fort Cummings was the most elaborate and best-walled fort in New Mexico. It covered an area 365 x 320 feet and was completely surrounded by a twelve-foot-high adobe wall. The main entrance was topped by a guard tower. Officers' quarters occupied the west side of the parade ground, the hospital the north side, and soldiers' quarters the east side. The various workshops, storerooms, offices, stables, and corrals extended along the south side of the fort.

Abandoned in August 1873, Fort Cummings was reoccupied in 1880, and then again abandoned in October 1886. Later it was used as a cattle corral by the Carpenter–Stanley Cattle Company. The spring was walled and covered, and the water piped to Florida.

Little remains of Fort Cummings today. A few weathered walls here and there among the mesquite and creosote bushes mark the site. The spring still flows, supplying water for the stock which now graze upon this "protector of the trail."

Fort Bayard

Fort Bayard, established in 1865 to protect the miners and settlers moving into the area following the Civil War, allowed the orderly development of what was to become New Mexico's most important mineral-producing area. Named for Capt. George D. Bayard who was wounded repeatedly during Indian forays and who died of wounds received in the Battle of Fredericksburg (Va.) during the Civil War, the fort was located about five miles southeast of Pinos Altos and about midway between the mining towns of Pinos Altos and Santa Rita. The site is about nine miles east of present-day Silver City, just north of State Highway 90.

The original fort consisted of log and adobe buildings forming a square around the parade ground. During its thirty-four year history as an army post, many changes and additions were made to the fort, including the building of two-storied officers' quarters. In 1899, the line troops were removed and the fort was officially designated as a U.S. Army General Hospital to treat tubercular soldiers. In 1920, the hospital was turned over to the Public Health Department; in 1922, to the U.S. Veterans Administration; and again, in 1966, to the State Health Department as a facility for the care of the aged and of tuberculosis cases. It can now accommodate more than 300 patients. The modern buildings are a far cry from the dirt-floored log and adobe buildings of the original fort.

HISTORY

Pre-Civil War Period. The period 1846 to 1861 was characterized by constant Indian warfare. Treaties were made, then broken. Forts were established, then abandoned, and new forts built as the military tried in vain to cope with the problem. Punitive expeditions proved ineffective as the Indians separated into small and predatory bands which overran the country.

Forts Union, Marcy, Fauntleroy, Craig, and Stanton were established during this period. Additional forts, whose sites have returned to the desert, are Fort Conrad (1851), on the Rio Grande about twenty-five miles south of Socorro; Fort Thorn (1853), on the Rio Grande about five miles north of Hatch; Fort Fillmore (1851), on the Rio Grande about seven miles south of Las Cruces; Fort Webster (1852), on the Mimbres River about one and one-half miles northwest of San Lorenzo; Fort McLane (1860), at Apache Tejo about four miles south of Hurley; and Fort Floyd (1857), on the Gila River about two miles south of Cliff.

Civil War Period. The outbreak of the Civil War in 1861 created a new problem on the frontier in New Mexico. Confederate military leaders moved quickly to seize control of the Southwest and California to cut off the supply of gold to the North and divert it to the Confederacy. Confederate troops under Col. J. B. Baylor occupied abandoned Fort Bliss at Franklin (El Paso), Texas on July 1, 1861. Baylor began his move northward along the Rio Grande on July 23 and quickly occupied Mesilla. Nearby Fort Fillmore was abandoned and the Union forces retreated toward Fort Stanton, but they were soon captured by Baylor's troops. Upon the fall of Fort Fillmore, Fort Stanton was hastily abandoned on August 2 and was taken over by the Confederates shortly thereafter.

Gen. H. H. Sibley arrived at Fort Bliss in December 1861 to assume command of the Confederate forces. Sibley's troops moved northward along the Rio Grande and were engaged in battle by Union troops from

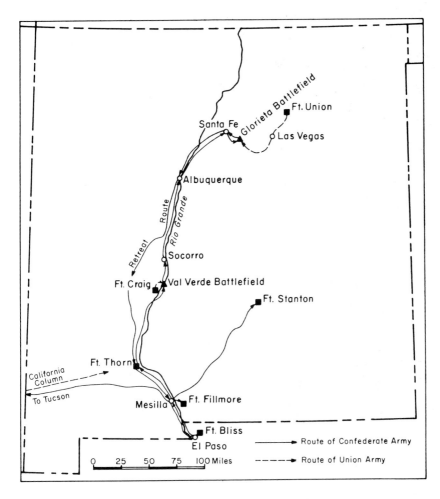

THE CONFEDERATE CAMPAIGN IN NEW MEXICO, 1861-1862

Fort Craig, under Gen. E. R. S. Canby, as they attempted to bypass the well-garrisoned post. The Battle of Val Verde took place four miles north of Fort Craig on February 21, 1862. After a day of bloody fighting, Sibley emerged the victor. He occupied Albuquerque on March 2, 1862, and Santa Fe on March 23. The Confederate forces then moved toward Fort Union in an attempt to gain complete control of the territory. On March 27 and 28, they were met by Union forces sent out from Fort Union and were defeated in battle near present-day Glorieta. Sibley then retreated to Fort Bliss.

While Sibley was thus engaged, another part of his army moved across what is now southwestern New Mexico and southeastern Arizona and occupied Tucson (Arizona). Gen. J. H. Carleton and his California

Column left Los Angeles on April 13 and cleared this area of Confederate troops, reaching the Rio Grande on August 7. Carleton reoccupied Fort Bliss, which had been abandoned by the Confederate troops in their retreat.

Post-Civil War Period. While the Union troops were preoccupied with the Confederates, the Indians stepped up their raids and depredations. With the passing of the Confederate threat, attention was once more focused on the Indian problem. A new plan was formulated which called for the capturing of the Indians and confining them to reservations. A reservation (Bosque Redondo) was established late in 1862 near present-day Fort Sumner, New Mexico, to which were eventually confined several thousand Navajos and Mescalero Apaches. This resettlement was not a success since the Apaches ran off and the Navajos suffered greatly from sickness and disease. A treaty was signed with the Navajos in 1868, and they were allowed to return to their homes, no longer a threat to the frontier. The Mescalero Apaches were finally settled on a reservation in their own country south of Fort Stanton, and the Jicarillas on a reservation west of Tierra Amarilla.

The Mimbreno, Mogollon, and Warm Springs Apaches of southwestern New Mexico were more of a problem. In 1871, a reservation and Fort Tularosa were established near present-day Aragon in western New Mexico. After a futile attempt to keep the Indians there, they were moved in 1874 to a new reservation and military post at Ojo Caliente, about forty miles northwest of present-day Truth or Consequences. This, too, proved a failure and the Apaches were moved to the San Carlos Reservation in what is now Arizona. During these attempts to locate the Apaches on reservations, various rebellious bands of Apaches led by Victorio, Nana, and Geronimo continued on the warpath. Geronimo and his band surrendered in 1886 and were imprisoned in Florida. After Geronimo's surrender, relative peace descended upon the frontier in New Mexico.

Established in the post-Civil War period were Forts Wingate (old and new), Selden, Cummings, and Bayard, as well as Fort Lowell (1868), near Tierra Amarilla; Fort Bascom (1863), on the Canadian River about eight miles north of Tucumcari; Fort Sumner (1862), on the Pecos River about five miles southeast of present-day Fort Sumner; Fort McRae (1863), on the Rio Grande about ten miles northeast of Truth or Consequences; and Fort West (1863), on the Gila River about two miles south of Cliff.

With the arrival of the railroad and cessation of hostilities with the Indians, a new era was begun. One by one, the old forts were abandoned: their need had passed. The colorful frontier forts of New Mexico are just a memory now.

Our National Heritage

National Forests in the so-called "desert" state of New Mexico cover more than 8.5 million acres, about 11 per cent of the state's area. National Monuments and Carlsbad Caverns National Park only extend over about 430 square miles but cover ten of New Mexico's most scenic areas that are of national geologic, archeologic, and historic interest. These are our national heritage, set aside by the federal government for the perpetual equal use of all Americans.

The forests cap the higher ranges of the state, except on windblown peaks that extend above the timberline. They provide protection for the watersheds that feed New Mexico's rivers, supply about 125 million board feet of cut timber each year, and yield forage for more than 150,000 cattle and sheep. Picnic nooks and camp grounds are plentiful, fish abound in the rushing mountain streams, and big game awaits the hunter throughout the forest lands. The primitive virgin wilderness is preserved in its natural state, accessible only by pack trip, in the Gila Wilderness area of the Diablo and Mogollon mountains north of Silver City and the Pecos Wilderness area east of Santa Fe in the Sangre de Cristo Mountains.

Incomparable Carlsbad Caverns is in the state's only National Park. National Monuments include the glistening gypsum dunes of White Sands, the volcanic cone of Capulin Mountain, the prehistoric ruins of Chaco Canyon, Aztec Ruins, Bandelier, and Gila Cliff Dwellings, the Spanish ruins at Gran Quivira, Inscription Rock at El Morro, and the crumbling walls of old Fort Union. In the near future, Valle Grande may be added to the National Park System and will include Valle Caldera, one of the world's largest volcanic calderas, a mountainous jumble with cool streams, thick coniferous forests, and lush high meadows.

NEW MEXICO'S BIG SHARE OF THE NATIONAL PARK SYSTEM

by H. V. Reeves, Jr.*

In contemplating the growth of cities and towns, the insatiable suburbs, congested streets and highways, the acres of dump yards for discarded automobiles, legions of billboards upstaging mountain ranges and seashores, and the melancholy predictions of demographers who say that within thirty years there will be twice as many of us, consider this: for New Mexico in particular, the outlook is not utterly bleak.

Some ninety years ago, without anything approaching the present-day horrible example before them, some farsighted, selfless, tireless individuals began to work to set aside areas of outstanding scenic, scientific, and

---

* National Park Service.

historical interest so that they would not be engulfed by humanity. Often against strong opposition, these benefactors succeeded in bringing about legislation that bounded many such areas and defined laws to protect them. The areas became national parks, monuments, and historic sites. And in 1916, the National Park Service, an agency of the U.S. Department of the Interior, was established to administer the units of the National Park System.

Today, other selfless individuals are contributing their time and effort to bring additional areas into the National Park System before they are lost forever. For example, Pecos ruins became a National Monument in late 1966 (see page 106).

Not every suggested area possesses the qualities that merit preservation, qualities of national significance. Proposed areas receive careful study before they are recommended for inclusion within the system—recommended to the Congress by the Secretary of the Interior. The Secretary's recommendations are based on those received from the Advisory Board on National Parks, Historic Sites, Buildings, and Monuments. This board is composed of eleven private citizens, each of whom is competent in one or more of the following fields: history, natural history, archeology, architecture, conservation, and recreation.

Diverse in character, New Mexico's ten units of the National Park System are of geologic, scenic, archeological, and historical interest. A visit to each unit will disclose the qualities that have been judged to be of national significance.

CARLSBAD CAVERNS NATIONAL PARK

Incomparable Carlsbad Caverns, in southeastern New Mexico, includes a single underground chamber so expansive that its floor could accommodate fourteen football fields and its ceiling could hold a 22-story building; other chambers that contain countless cave formations of great variety of shape and color; cool and naturally circulating fresh air; and a system of lighting that reveals the beauty and spaciousness most effectively.

Since the temperature within the Caverns remains at about 56°F the year round, warm clothing is needed. Comfortable shoes, too, for the four-hour, three-mile complete tour, which starts at the natural entrance. Shorter trips, the Big Room tours that start at the elevators in the visitor center, take in only a part of the underground chambers. All tours are under leadership of competent park guides who answer questions and explain the earth processes that have resulted in the caverns and their amazing decorations.

From the natural entrance, the immense main corridor of the Caverns is followed downward 829 feet for one and three-quarters miles. This brings visitors to the most scenic rooms (the Green Lake Room, King's Palace, Queen's Chamber, and Papoose Room), where the stalactites, stalagmites, and helictites reach their peak in numbers, shapes, and delicate coloring. The trail leads upward 80 feet from the Papoose Room to the lunchroom. Near the lunchroom is the Big Room, the most majestic of the Caverns'

HALL OF GIANTS IN CARLSBAD CAVERNS NATIONAL PARK

chambers. The trail around its perimeter, one and a quarter miles long, encompasses a floor space of fourteen acres.

Completing the circuit of the Big Room and returning to the lunchroom, visitors may either walk or board an elevator and ride smoothly back to the surface.

How were the Caverns formed? The story began about 240 million years ago, during the Permian Period. At that time, the two limestone formations in which the caverns occur—the Tansill Formation and Capitan Limestone—were deposited as part of an organic reef complex at the edge of a warm shallow sea.

During subsequent periods, other seas brought in sedimentary material that covered the reef. About 60 million years ago, earth movements, which were responsible for the uplift of the area, fractured the reef and permitted surrounding ground water to enter along fracture lines and begin work in fashioning the caverns. The water at first dissolved small crevices in the limestone. As more water came in, the crevices enlarged to cavities, called solution pockets. Then the walls, floors, and ceilings of the pockets dissolved and collapsed, joining the pockets, while the solution process continued, eventually forming the huge rooms seen today.

Beginning about 3 million years ago and into recent times, the uplift of the local Guadalupe Mountains and changing climates lowered the water table. Water that had been inside the caverns drained away and was replaced by air. Most solution stopped, but large sections of partly dissolved walls and ceilings collapsed under their own weight. Stability was

77

finally achieved, however, and probably no rock has fallen within the caverns during the last several thousand years.

Even before the collapsing ended, another phase of cavern development had begun. Rain water and snow melt slowly seeped into the caverns. Droplets of water, each holding a minute quantity of dissolved limestone, appeared upon the ceilings. Exposed to the air, the droplets evaporated and left their mineral content as calcite and aragonite—crystalline forms of limestone. Over centuries, this process of evaporation and deposition has built a myriad of crystalline stalactites of all shapes and sizes. Water that dripped to the floor evaporated and deposited the calcite and aragonite to build stalagmites. When joined together, stalactites and stalagmites become columns, or pillars. In the scenic rooms, conditions existed that brought about the creation of helictites—twisted formations that seem to defy gravity in their growth. Color in the cave formations, shades of brown, red, and yellow, result from the presence of small amounts of iron oxide and other minerals.

Carlsbad Caverns National Park offers more than the caverns themselves. Each evening from April to October, bats in incredible numbers spiral upward out of the Caverns' entrance and fly southward over the rim of the escarpment to feed in the valleys of the Black and Pecos rivers. They return just before dawn, diving swiftly and from high altitudes into the entrance. Flying directly to the bat cave, they spend each day hanging head downward in dense clusters from the walls and ceilings. The bat cave itself is not open to visitors. A park naturalist explains the bat flight and discusses the bats in detail in a talk given at the entrance to the Caverns each evening before the flight begins.

The nature trail, a half mile loop that begins and ends near the entrance to the Caverns, guides the visitor to many of the desert plants of the region. The park is visited by more than half a million people each year, and yet the delicate cave formations and the natural beauties remain unmarred.

WHITE SANDS NATIONAL MONUMENT

White Sands National Monument, fifteen miles southwest of Alamogordo, is another area of great interest to the geologist and biologist. But its strangeness, the graceful contours of its snow-white dunes, and the peculiar adaptations of some of the plants and animals that live among its dunes are appreciated as fully by the nonscientist. More than 370,000 visitors come to marvel at the White Sands each year.

The Monument, some 230 square miles in extent, preserves the most impressive part of the world's largest gypsum desert. This is a glistening sea of pure gypsum sand that the wind has drifted into huge dunes that are almost bare of vegetation except along the fringes. Wavelike, the restive dunes move slowly before the prevailing winds, covering and uncovering the few plants that lie in their way. And wavelike, their surfaces trace the vagaries of indecisive breezes in tiny parallel ripplelike ridges.

Because of the almost constant wind and resulting gradual advance of the dunes, most of the plants that are able to establish themselves in the open flats between the dunes eventually become buried. A few species, however, are able to survive the irresistible march of the sand. Through rapid growth and elongation of the stems, the struggling crowns remain on top of the rising crests of the dunes. Plants with stems more than forty feet long have been found. As the dunes continue forward under the pressure of the wind, they leave the plants elevated on columns of compacted gypsum bound by their adventitious roots.

Animals, too, have become adapted to their unusual surroundings. The small creatures, lizards, mice, and others, are picked off easily by such predators as foxes, coyotes, and hawks when they are conspicuous. Thus, through the centuries, only the lighter-colored individuals have survived among the dunes and, through many generations, have developed pale and elusive animals that blend inconspicuously with their white surroundings. Pocket mice are a good example of this. Among the white dunes, the pocket mice are white; in the nearby red hills, they are a rusty color; and on the beds of black lava a few miles north of the sand, the pocket mice are very dark.

A visitor to White Sands National Monument should stop at the visitor center, where exhibits explain the geology of the duneland and others describe the plants and animals that are able to live there.

But how and from where did this natural wonder come? The dunes of gypsum lie in the Tularosa Basin, which stretches for more than 100 miles between two north-south mountain ranges. All sides of the valley slope gently inward, forming the basin, with Lake Lucero, its lowest point, at the southwest end of the Monument. This valley was formed hundreds of centuries ago, when a great section of the earth's crust settled to form the type of basin known geologically as a graben.

High above the basin floor, beds of gypsum are found to the north in the mountain ranges flanking the valley. Similar gypsum beds lie far beneath the floor of the basin. Thus, it was once a part of the high plateau, a great blocklike section that slowly sank to form the basin at its present level.

Percolating water from seasonal rains and melting snow carries tons of gypsum, in solution, from the highlands at the north end of the basin into Lake Lucero. During much of the year, cloudless skies and warm dry winds evaporate Lake Lucero, and it shrinks to a crystal-encrusted marsh. Capillarity draws the gypsum-laden underground water to the surface; it, too, evaporates, depositing its burden of gypsum throughout the extensive "alkali flats." The persistent southwest wind picks up the particles of gypsum and whirls them away, adding them to the gleaming white dunes, the accumulation of centuries.

The best ways to see the dunes are by car and by foot. Along the drive that leads into the heart of the duneland are numbered posts that correspond to numbered paragraphs in the Monument's informational folder. These paragraphs explain the features that are of particular significance. At pull-outs along the drive, park the car and walk among the dunes.

Capulin Mountain National Monument, in the northeast part of the state, is an area of geologic interest that presents still another aspect of the science of the earth. It contains the cone of an extinct volcano, one of the most symmetrical of the geologically recent cinder cones in the United States. Its conical form rises more than 1000 feet above its base. The irregular rim is about one mile in circumference, and the crater is about 415 feet in depth, as measured from the highest part of the rim. Some 40,000 people a year visit the Monument.

The mountain consists chiefly of loose cinders, ash, and other rock debris of volcanic explosions. These materials were spewed out by a series of successive eruptions, probably of considerable duration. The coarse materials fell back around the vent, piling up to form the conical mound. Dust and other fine materials were carried away by the wind. After the eruptions, vegetation gained a foothold on the steep, unstable flanks of the cone, so that in time the slopes became stabilized. Geological studies indicate that the volcano probably was active about 7000 years ago.

Capulin Mountain is of special interest, partly because it represents the last stages of a great period of volcanic activity that was widespread throughout western North America. Evidences of this older and more intense activity can be seen from the top of Capulin Mountain in the scores of other nearby volcanic hills and peaks. The largest of these is the Sierra Grande, an extinct volcano rising 4000 feet above the surrounding plain; it is ten miles to the southeast. Northwest of Capulin are a number of mesas that are capped with black lava, the largest of which are Barella, Raton, and Johnson. Fishers Peak, south of Trinidad, Colorado, is on a similar mesa. The famous Spanish Peaks, northwest of Trinidad, are a pair of extinct volcanoes.

In this great volcanic area, the lava erupted in a succession of flows. The series of eruptions were separated by long periods of inactivity. During these inactive times, erosion cut valleys and wore down parts of the old lava sheets. This action formed new channels and lower terrain over which succeeding lava flows spread. This process was repeated at least three times. The oldest lavas, which have been exposed by erosion, are found on the tops of the highest mesas. The last series of eruptions created Capulin Mountain; they were ejections mostly of cinders and ash, with less lava flow than in the preceding volcanic activity. These cinder-and-ash eruptions were so recent, geologically, that some of the nearby, bare, steep-sided cinder cones appear as if they had just cooled.

The National Park Service has constructed a road up the mountain to the rim of the crater. And from the parking area at the rim, two trails lead to the most interesting points on the mountain. One trail, self-guiding, makes the complete one-mile circuit of the crater along the rim. A guide booklet, keyed to numbered stakes that have been set at places along the trail, explains the features of particular significance—both on the mountain and in the distance. The other trail, less scenic, provides a rare op-

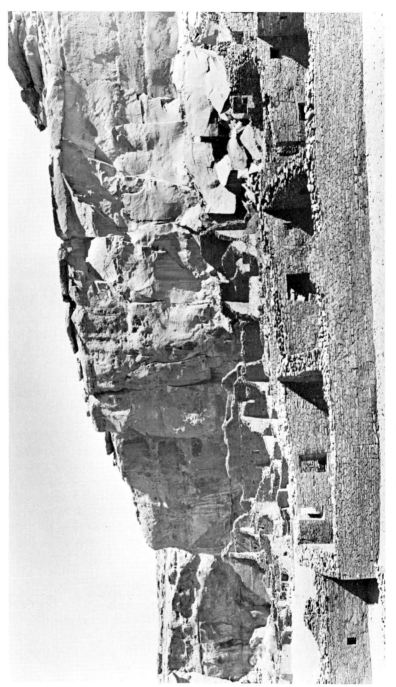

View of Chaco Canyon National Monument

portunity to see a volcanic mountain from the inside out, for it leads down to the bottom of the crater.

Chaco Canyon National Monument

Rich in areas of geological interest, New Mexico is equally rich in areas of archeological interest. Four of these are preserved as units of the National Park System.

Chaco Canyon National Monument, in the northwestern part of the state, contains more than a dozen large prehistoric ruins and hundreds of smaller archeological sites. These ruins are considered to be without equal north of central Mexico. No other archeological area in the Southwest exhibits such a high development of prehistoric Pueblo civilization. Most of the sites lie within a strip of land about eight miles long and two miles wide, through which Chaco Canyon runs. Although the Monument is relatively isolated, it is open year around and is visited by about 22,000 people annually.

The most imposing and best known of the ruins is Pueblo Bonito. Built between 800 and 900 years ago, this 4- and 5-story village covered more than three acres and contained about 800 rooms and 32 kivas, or ceremonial chambers. Archeologist Neil M. Judd, of the National Museum, who conducted some of the late excavations, has said that Pueblo Bonito was the largest apartment house built anywhere in the world prior to 1887, estimating that at one time it housed 1200 people.

Earliest of the Chaco sites, small villages of crude pit houses were occupied during 600 to 800 A.D. Archeologists, studying changes in masonry style, pottery types, and other remains, have pieced together the development of the culture of the inhabitants of Chaco Canyon over a period of six centuries.

After Chaco Canyon's cultural high point was reached in the 1100's, a gradual decline set in. The population decreased, and in the 1200's, the region was abandoned. During this same century, other Pueblo centers within the San Juan Basin were also deserted.

Various theories have been advanced to explain this exodus: soil erosion, warlike enemies, poor facilities for urban sanitation, drought, and intervillage warfare. One or a combination of these factors might have been instrumental in bringing about the abandonment of the region.

Aztec Ruins National Monument

Aztec Ruins National Monument, at Aztec in the northwestern corner of the state, was set aside to preserve an outstanding example of classical Pueblo construction, one of the largest pre-Spanish villages in the Southwest. More than 40,000 visitors come to the Monument each year.

Tree-ring dates indicate that most of the big central pueblo was rapidly constructed during the period 1106 to 1121. At this time, the people of Aztec were influenced by the cultural center to the south, Chaco Canyon. During the last half of the 1100's, after the decline of Chaco Canyon had begun, the people of Aztec began to look toward the north, and by 1200, Mesa Verde ideas dominated the region. Aztec was abandoned by about 1300, as was the rest of the general region.

Of particular interest at Aztec Ruins National Monument is the reconstructed Great Kiva. The Pueblo Indians built separate rooms, now known as kivas, for ceremonial purposes. During the period of Chaco influence, the people at Aztec constructed a very large circular building, 48 feet in diameter, in their plaza. Its features differ from those of the small kivas and establish it as a Great Kiva, similar to those at Chaco. The Great Kivas represent the peak of religious architecture among the Pueblos. The Great Kiva at Aztec was completely restored in 1934 by Earl H. Morris, of the American Museum of Natural History.

BANDELIER NATIONAL MONUMENT

Bandelier National Monument, forty-six miles west of Santa Fe, preserves the ruins of dwellings and other structures that were erected by Indians who lived in the area until about 1550 A.D. Almost 100,000 people visit the Monument each year.

When many of the ancient Pueblo Indian centers were abandoned in the late thirteenth century, the people moved to locations where the water supply was more constant. A favorable area was the upper Rio Grande Valley in what is now New Mexico. One of the later flowerings of Pueblo culture occurred here. The ruins within Bandelier are representative of this phase of Pueblo development.

In Frijoles Canyon, the Indians chose the location of their homes well. The creek that runs through the canyon flows all year. On the canyon floor and mesa top there was land suitable to the cultivation of crops. And the canyon walls of soft tuff (consolidated volcanic ash) could easily be hollowed out by the Indians with their harder stone tools in fashioning storage rooms behind dwellings built against the cliff.

Cliff ruins, or talus villages, extend along the base of the northern wall of the canyon for about two miles. Other ruins are located on the floor of the canyon. The houses of stone masonry were irregularly terraced, from one to three stories in height. Some hollowed recesses at the base of the cliff also were used for dwelling rooms.

Like the other pueblo dwellers, the Frijoles inhabitants were farmers, raising the usual corn, beans, and squash. They used cotton cloth, which has been found in the ruins and which suggests that they had the loom. Since the growing season in the high Frijoles country is short, they probably obtained their cotton by trade with Indians who lived farther south. They made pottery decorated with glaze paint.

For a few centuries, the Indian farmers lived in the canyons, built villages, honeycombed the cliffs with artificial caves, and tilled the soil. But with the passing years, drought, soil-eroding floods, soil depletion, famine, and possibly disease—singly or in combination—forced the canyon dwellers again to seek new homes. Descendants of these Indians still live in nearby modern pueblos along the Rio Grande.

CLIFF HOUSES IN FRIJOLES CANYON, BANDELIER NATIONAL MONUMENT

About ninety per cent of Bandelier National Monument is, and will remain, a wilderness. The rugged and scenic back country is accessible by about sixty miles of maintained trails, leading to such features as Alamo Canyon, the Stone Lions, Painted Cave, the Pueblo ruins of San Miguel and Yapashi, and White Rock Canyon of the Rio Grande.

VALLE GRANDE

Another area has been considered as an addition to the National Park System in New Mexico. A 1963 bill introduced in Congress would establish Valle Grande–Bandelier National Park, about forty-six miles west of Santa Fe. Valle Grande is part of the Valle Caldera, which is among the world's largest and has been the site of extensive studies of calderas (the collapsed summits of volcanoes). Lessons learned there have been applied in recognizing and investigating calderas in other places. Bandelier National Monument, primarily of archeological significance, lies to the east of the

canyon-cut rim of the caldera. As written, the bill would have incorporated the Monument in the proposed national park.

GILA CLIFF DWELLINGS NATIONAL MONUMENT

Gila Cliff Dwellings National Monument, forty-seven miles north of Silver City and at the edge of the Gila Wilderness Area, contains a series of ruins that portray the development of the agricultural Indians who lived south of the Mogollon Mountains. Specifically, the ruins represent a branch of the generalized culture known as Mogollon. Although part of the road to the Monument was paved in 1963, the last four-mile stretch is still primitive and should not be attempted in an ordinary passenger car except during the summer and in dry weather. In spite of the difficult road, more than 23,000 people visited the Monument during 1965. The last four miles of the road have been recently paved:

The earliest ruin yet found within the Monument is a Mogollon pit house of a type that was made about 500 A.D. It is roundish and, on the east side, has a narrow ramplike entrance some two feet wide and ten feet long. The people of this period did only a little farming (corn and beans), a little hunting, and gathered much uncultivated plant food. They made a fairly good plain-brown pottery and undoubtedly were skilled in a number of crafts whose products have since disappeared. Such things as nets and snares, baskets, and wooden tools last but a short time in open sites.

Other, later, pit house types may be seen in the Monument. Pit houses were prevalent in the area until about 1000 A.D., when influences from the Anasazi (Pueblo) Indians of the northern part of the South-west began to affect the Mogollon people.

Square houses, built above the ground, became the style; some were of masonry, some of adobe construction, and some were built of wattle (wooden rods and twigs). A new type of pottery was also introduced at about the same time: white with black designs.

The principal ruins in the Monument are the cliff dwellings, which were built during the twelfth and thirteenth centuries. They, too, re-flect the northern pueblo influence. About forty rooms, remarkably well preserved, are fitted into a series of chambers, or caves, in a low cliff of Gila Conglomerate. By about the beginning of the fifteenth century, the area was abandoned by the farming Indians.

GRAN QUIVIRA NATIONAL MONUMENT

Significant chapters in the absorbing history of New Mexico were written at three sites that have been made units of the National Park System.

Gran Quivira National Monument, near the center of the state south-east of Mountainair, preserves the ruins of a frontier Spanish mission that had been built, used, and abandoned by 1675. The Monument contains twenty-one ruined house mounds of Indian pueblos and ruins of two mission churches. It was the presence of the Indians at this location, of course, that attracted the Franciscan missionaries.

The earliest Indian pueblo in the Monument was founded about 1300 A.D.; by the 1600's, the village, with several structures, had become the largest in the region. It was conveniently located on the south side of a hill near the cultivated fields in the surrounding lowlands. Water was a problem then as now. The Indians solved this as best they could by digging shallow wells at the base of the hill, about one mile west of the pueblo.

The first known specific reference to Gran Quivira was made in 1630 by Fray Alonso de Benavides, a Franciscan missionary. He called the pueblo the "Village of the Humanas," and referred to the church there as having been built by Father Francisco Letrado in 1629 and dedicated to San Isidro. Humanas, now misnamed "Gran Quivira," was later administered from the mission of San Gregorio de Abo, some forty miles to the north. In 1659, Father Diego de Santander was assigned to Humanas. Construction of the mission buildings, which he rededicated to San Buenaventura, was completed by him.

The Franciscans had a pronounced influence upon the Pueblo Indians. They stimulated trade with Mexico and the pueblos farther north. They imported wine grapes and cultivated them, and they introduced domesticated sheep, goats, cattle, and horses.

Sometime between 1672 and 1675, the pueblo and mission at Humanas were abandoned because of Apache raids, drought, and crop failures. The people first moved to the Rio Grande near the present town of Socorro. A few continued to El Paso del Norte, where, in 1680, they were joined by those from Socorro, who had fled with the Spaniards from the Pueblo Revolt of that year.

EL MORRO NATIONAL MONUMENT

El Morro National Monument, southwest of Grants near Ramah, was established to preserve the famous Inscription Rock, register of Indians, Spaniards, and westward-moving pioneers. About 22,000 people now visit the Monument each year.

El Morro, or Inscription Rock, is a massive mesa point of sandstone. Rising some 200 feet above the valley floor, it forms a striking landmark. From its summit, rain and melted snow drain into a natural basin at the foot of the cliff, creating a constant and dependable supply of water in a region where water is scarce. The route from Acoma to the Zuni pueblos led directly past the mesa. It was a regular camping place for Spanish conquistadores and, later, for travelers from the east.

On the top of El Morro lie ruins of Indian pueblos, abandoned long before the coming of the Spaniards. And carved in the sandstone are numerous petroglyphs left by these ancient people, ancestors of the modern Zunis. Perhaps it was the petroglyphs that prompted later travelers to record their names and thoughts on the rock.

The first known historical mention of El Morro is found in the journal of Diego Pérez de Luxán, chronicler of the Espejo Expedition of 1583. Luxán stopped there for water on March 11 of that year.

89

PART OF THE POOL AND CLIFF AT EL MORRO

The oldest dated inscription at El Morro was made in 1605 by don Juan de Oñate, first governor of New Mexico. Returning from an expedition to the mouth of the Colorado River, he camped at El Morro and carved this inscription in Spanish: "Passed by here the Adelantado Don Juan de Oñate from the discovery of the Sea of the South, the 16th of April of 1605." The "Sea of the South" was the Gulf of California.

If don Diego de Vargas, the most famous Spanish governor of New Mexico, seems boastful in the message he left at El Morro, who can blame him? His words, in English, read, "Here was the General Don Diego de Vargas, who conquered for our Holy Faith and for the Royal Crown all of New Mexico at his own expense, year of 1692." Twelve years earlier, the great Pueblo Indian Revolt had driven the Spaniards from New Mexico. More than 400, including 23 priests, had lost their lives, and the surviving Spaniards, some 1100, had fled to El Paso del Norte. De Vargas restored order, without further bloodshed, in 1692.

After the occupation of Santa Fe by the army of Gen. Stephen W. Kearny in August 1846, details of United States troops were dispatched to explore various parts of New Mexico. Probably the first to visit El Morro was Lt. J. H. Simpson, accompanied by the artist R. H. Kern, who copied some of the early inscriptions in September 1849. Then the names of other soldiers, traders, Indian agents, surveyors, emigrants who were traveling westward, and settlers were added to the rock.

Since the establishment of the Monument by Presidential proclamation in 1906, inscribing on the face of the cliff has been prohibited. If the Monument had not been established and the law not passed, this fascinating part of the history of the Southwest would surely have been lost.

Fort Union National Monument

Fort Union National Monument, twenty-six miles northeast of Las Vegas and on the route of the old Santa Fe Trail where the mountains meet the plains, preserves the ruins of a famous frontier Army post. As a base of operations for military and civilian ventures in New Mexico from 1851 to 1891, Fort Union helped to direct the course of events in the formative years of the Southwest. More than 11,000 visitors come to the Monument each year.

Five years after the conquest of New Mexico by the United States in the war with Mexico, Col. E. V. Sumner moved some of his troops from Fort Marcy, in Santa Fe, to the site of Fort Union and there began construction of log buildings on the west side of Coyote Creek. This was the first Fort Union.

The first post took an active part in protecting settlers and traders from Indian raids during the 1850's. Mounted patrols of dragoons made many expeditions into the mountains against the warring Apaches and Utes and out onto the plains to pursue Comanche war parties.

Fort Union was also charged with supply and support of many outlying military posts, such as Fort Defiance and Fort Craig. The Quartermaster Depot at Fort Union in later years came to be the hub of all Army supply services in the Southwest.

During the first three decades of its life, Fort Union saw the great Conestoga wagons and prairie schooners of the Santa Fe Trail caravans pass in increasing numbers. By the outbreak of the Civil War, enterprising traders were hauling more than ten million dollars' worth of goods from Missouri each year. The fort provided escorts for caravans and when requested by apprehensive company or postal officials, escorts for stage-coaches of the Independence–Santa Fe Mail. Century-old tracks of the Santa Fe Trail can be still seen near Fort Union.

The start of the Civil War in 1861 brought new activity to the fort. Immediate invasion of New Mexico by Confederate forces from Texas was expected. Gen. E. R. S. Canby, commanding Union troops in the territory, began construction of an earthwork fortification in a defensive position about a mile from the original fort. The ditches, parapets, and bomb-proofs of this redoubt were completed late in 1861.

The Texas column was not slow in coming. By March 1862, these invaders under Gen. Henry H. Sibley had defeated a Union force at Val Verde, had frightened the defenders from Albuquerque and Santa Fe into inaction, and were marching eastward across the mountains toward the final stronghold, Fort Union. On March 10, the First Regiment of Colorado Volunteers, under Col. J. P. Slough, arrived at Fort Union as reinforcements. And on March 22, Colonel Slough led his 1342 men out of the fort to meet the advancing Confederates. In a two-day battle fought in Apache Canyon and Glorieta Pass, the Union forces defeated the Confederates, thus saving Fort Union for the federal cause.

From 1863 to 1869, the garrisons at Fort Union were chiefly occupied in a construction program that produced most of the adobe-walled buildings whose ruins may now be seen. Fort Union then returned to its earlier mission of a base for Indian fighting.

The usefulness of Fort Union was reduced with the final submission of the Indians and with the arrival of the railhead at Las Vegas in 1879. The huge fort was demoted to caretaker status in the 1880's and was abandoned in 1891.

At each of these New Mexico units of the National Park System, as at other units throughout the nation, trained personnel of the National Park Service—archeologists, historians, naturalists, and park rangers—are on duty. Their purpose is to make the visitor's trip rewarding. This they do through museum exhibits, guided walks and self-guiding trails, campfire talks, and publications.

Here in New Mexico, then, escape the irritations that seem to go with progress. Awaiting the traveler are unspoiled places where he can surround himself with the quiet majesty of nature, walk the paths made by prehistoric people, camp where the Spanish *conquistadores* camped, stroll among the ruins of buildings erected by the men who helped to fashion the Southwest.

FOREST LANDS ABOVE THE DESERT
by Ruth Bush Jones*

Today, as in earlier times, people of New Mexico look to their mountains with a new and greater appreciation of their forest land heritage. Today, also, people seek aesthetic values of peace, beauty, and serenity found in nature's solitudes, in addition to forest products for economic use. Basic to the enjoyment of the high country are the forest treasures of clear, pure water . . . of wild game and birds . . . of trees for shade and solitude, fuel, shelter, and forest products . . . of grass and browse for cattle, sheep, horses, and wildlife . . . of magnificent grandeur and panoramic vistas. These basic treasures coupled with understanding of the purposes and many benefits of the National Forests bring true recreation to the visitor.

The high country of New Mexico, much of it in the National Forests, is entrusted by law to the care and administration of the U.S. Forest Service, an agency of the Department of Agriculture. These vast public properties located in several sections of the state are administered as Carson, Santa Fe, Cibola, Lincoln, Gila, Apache, and Coronado National Forests, the latter two lying primarily in Arizona and being directed from there rather than from New Mexico. Visitors to New Mexico traveling along main highways see the high forest country outlining the horizon and often regard the lofty masses of rugged rock as unapproachable and lacking in friendliness.

"Not so," says the Forest Ranger. There are broad highways welcoming the traveler into the high country where forest trees stretch to the sky. There are cool invigorating streams sparkling clear and clean from mountain fastnesses and developed campgrounds and picnic areas ready for use. Outdoor recreation from simple relaxing and picnicking under a pine tree to the most strenuous of wilderness backpacking or horseback riding, winter sports, and skiing awaits the visitor. There is fishing in mountain streams and in big open lakes or in precious, secluded mountain lakes. And for those who like their surroundings interpreted for them, there are nature trails and/or forest naturalists to explain local rock formations, vegetation, and the natural and human history of the immediate country.

The Forest Ranger asks only that each visitor do his share in cleaning up a camp or picnic site and being *sure* that camp fires, matches, and cigarettes are thoroughly extinguished: "Keep Your National Forest Green and Clean!"

CARSON NATIONAL FOREST

Located in north-central New Mexico, with headquarters at Taos, the Carson National Forest nurtures and cradles the Rio Grande as it leaves its birthplace in Colorado en route to the south. Carrying water from high country snow melt, the Carson adds precious, clear water from its

---

* Forest Service, Southwestern Region, U.S. Dept. of Agriculture.

MAP OF NATIONAL FORESTS IN NEW MEXICO

high mountain streams and lakes to the Rio Grande in support of the prosperous communities along its way. The Carson includes some of the highest water-producing lands in the state and is the source of several permanent streams and lakes.

Named in honor of Kit Carson, the noted scout, Carson National Forest offers some of the most spectacular mountain scenery in the Southwest, including the Sangre de Cristo Mountains, Red River Canyon, and Wheeler Peak, which at 13,160 feet is the highest point in New Mexico. Part of the famed Pecos Wilderness Area and the Wheeler Peak Wild Area are included in this Forest and are available to those willing and able to hike, ride a horse, or pack into the rugged mountain country. For the winter sports enthusiast, the Red River Ski Area, Sipapu Winter Sports

Area, and Taos Ski Valley operate in part within the Carson National Forest and offer some of the finest alpine skiing in the Southwest.

Good roads lead the visitor to Spanish and Indian villages where life and culture are almost unchanged since the ancient and comparatively recent days of settlement. Towns with singing-sounding names like Picurís, Taos Pueblo, Las Trampas, Truchas, Santa Barbara, and Tres Ritos nestle along forest streams and add charm and beauty to a scenic trip in the northern Sangre de Cristo range (name given to the mountains by early Spanish settlers, meaning *Blood of Christ*. The analogy relates to the reddish glow that sometimes colors the mountains at sunset.). Radiating from Taos are roads leading into the eastern half of the Forest, bringing the traveler into fascinating and colorful country. Taos Canyon, Arroyo Hondo, Questa, and the Red River country abound in old mining ghost towns, Indian ruins, and legendary Spanish villages located in canyons and on mountain tops.

The high range rising between the Rio Grande and the Chama River to the west is the major part of the western half of the Carson National Forest. Tres Piedras, El Rito, La Madera, Canjilon, Lagunitas, and San Antonio are a few of the picturesque communities here. Farther to the west is the Jicarilla Division of the Carson, the high mountain country adjacent to the Jicarilla Apache Reservation. Bisected by State Highway 17 between Farmington and Chama, this section is a test of true pioneering skill for the traveler who is willing to follow dim tracks of roads and trails to enjoy the Forest. However, modern civilization is introduced by the 150 oil and gas wells in this area, even though the country is rugged and broken.

Carson National Forest is a trout fisherman's delight. For the hunter, Rocky Mountain mule deer, elk, and antelope are found in all parts of the Forest. Small game is plentiful, and rabbits provide many hours of hunting pleasure. Beaver, muskrat, mink, weasel, marten, and skunk are the principal fur bearers, and turkey, grouse, ducks, geese, quail, and doves make up the game bird population. Predators include the mountain lion, bobcat, coyote, and fox.

More than 40 developed camp and picnic grounds, most of which are accessible year round, welcome the visitor. Among them, Echo Amphitheater picnic ground on U.S. Highway 84, south of Canjilon, is a striking natural echo chamber formed by centuries of wind and water erosion in the rugged sandstone rock. "If you stand near the chamber, you only have to whisper, and your words come back in a spooky echo."

About five miles south on U.S. Highway 84 is the Ghost Ranch Museum, with live native Southwestern animals and conservation exhibits, including a living and growing display showing on-the-ground Forest Service Multiple Use Management of the mythical Beaver National Forest, the "smallest National Forest in the world."

Ranger stations at Canjilon, El Rito, Gobernador, Penasco, Questa, Taos, and Tres Piedras provide local information and recreation maps.

ECHO AMPHITHEATER SURROUNDS PART OF THE TRAIL TO CAMPGROUND

SANTA FE NATIONAL FOREST

The Santa Fe National Forest, with headquarters in Santa Fe, lies directly south of the Carson National Forest on both sides of the Rio Grande and is the center of a region rich in natural resources as well as historic and geologic interests. The two divisions of the Forest contain the high mountains to the east and west in the central section of the state. The Pecos Division to the east of the Rio Grande is the location of the major part of the Pecos Wilderness Area, one of the earliest of such areas to be established.

The Pecos Division is so named because the Pecos River, which later joins the Rio Grande in Texas, heads among its towering mountains in a beautiful alpine basin sometimes called the *Pecos Horseshoe*. The Pecos River is one of the state's largest streams and supplies some of its most important irrigation projects. This division of the Forest includes the southern part of the Sangre de Cristo range and was first known as the Pecos River Forest Reserve, established in 1892—the oldest National Forest in the Southwest. The division abounds in clear, cold mountain lakes and streams. Truchas Lakes, Pecos Baldy, Stewart Lake, Spirit Lake, and Lost Lake, as well as many mountain streams, lure not only the fisherman but the hiker and camper to their wilderness beauty.

Twenty-three developed campgrounds and picnic areas located in cool glades are ready for the visitor along roads leading into the Forest from Santa Fe, Pecos, Glorieta, Las Vegas, and other communities. Skiing and winter sports are available at the Santa Fe Ski Basin northeast of Santa Fe; the chair lift operates year around for those who wish merely to view the spectacular scenery. The Pecos Division watersheds of the Santa Fe National Forest, like the eastern section of the Carson, contribute generously to the water flow of the Rio Grande.

Wild game, game birds; and fishing attract visitors at all times of the year, while the golden hues of the aspen in the autumn tempt artists and photographers to record on canvas and film nature's fall colors. A trip just before the winter snows to the aspen country of the Santa Fe National Forest is a must. Ranger stations are located at Santa Fe, Las Vegas, and Pecos.

West of the Rio Grande are the Jemez Mountains, which form the Jemez Division of the Santa Fe National Forest. The Jemez country is a favorite area for fishermen and hunters. For the sturdy hiker and picnicker, there are hundreds of fascinating points to visit and peaks to climb. Capulin Peak, Dead Man's Peak, Nacimiento Peak, and Cerro Pedernal are a few of the exciting ones. The Jemez country contains the San Pedro Parks

AN IZAAK WALTON ALONG THE PECOS RIVER

Wild Area, northeast of Cuba where San Gregorio Lake is waiting for the fisherman or hiker willing to walk or ride horseback. This section abounds in unique geologic formations—Battleship Rock, Tent Rocks, Tea-kettle Rock, to name a few.

Eighteen developed camping and picnicking areas welcome the visitor to the Jemez Division. Youth groups also favor the Jemez for their summer camping. Boy Scouts, Girl Scouts, Camp Fire Girls, YMCA, and others have camps adjacent to the Santa Fe National Forest. Timber production, wildlife habitat management, livestock grazing, and watershed protection are among the activities of the Jemez Division, while visitors and travelers enjoy the forest, the streams, and the unique scenery. Ranger stations are at Jemez Springs, Cuba, Espanola, and Coyote.

CIBOLA NATIONAL FOREST

A mountain playground for people who live or visit near U.S. Highway 66 is Cibola National Forest, with headquarters in Albuquerque. Embracing the Sandias, Manzanos, and Gallinas Peak areas east of the Rio Grande in central New Mexico, this Forest also includes most of the mountain ranges in the west-central section of the state, the San Mateo Mountains, with 11,389-foot Mount Taylor, and the Datil, Magdalena, and Zuni ranges.

Outdoor recreation is the fastest growing use of the Cibola National Forest and more than a million visits are made each year to this popular Forest. The name is a Zuni Indian word, pronounced SEE-bo-lah, meaning *buffalo*. Buffalo may have roamed the Cibola in years past, but today's big game animals making the Cibola their home are the Rocky Mountain bighorn sheep, Rocky Mountain mule deer, white-tailed deer, elk, antelope, and bear. Game birds include turkey, grouse, quail, and dove; spring and fall migrations of ducks and geese use the Cibola as a resting place. There are 18 campgrounds with 249 family units and 14 picnic grounds with 382 family units scattered through the vast domain of the Cibola National Forest.

Sandia Crest in the Sandia Mountains east of Albuquerque is a goal for many travelers. Here on this 10,678-foot mountain top, there is a breathtaking view of the middle Rio Grande Valley and the Estancia Valley—a jet age view of nearly 10,000 square miles. The visitor stands on rocks which in eons past were under the sea, as indicated by fossils found on the peak. Recent recreation developments have been made at the Sandia Ski Area where a new 7450-foot double chair lift will carry 700 riders an hour on a 1650-foot vertical rise to the restaurant and upper terminal on Sandia Crest. A tramway ascends the west face of the Sandias to meet the Ski Area chair lift at the Crest.

The fabled Manzano Mountains rising above the plains to the west of State Highway 10 and south of U.S. Highway 66 are fast becoming a haven for the camper, picnicker, or sightseer willing to follow secondary roads to find the perfect spot to enjoy the forest. Capillo Peak, 9368 feet high, Mosca Peak, Cerro Blanco, and Manzano Peak lure the mountain climber. Legends surrounding the old Spanish communities of Tajique, Torreon, and Manzano are exciting campfire stories after a day spent exploring the high country.

West of the Rio Grande, the San Mateo Mountains north of Grants and the Zuni Mountains forming the backbone of the Continental Divide southeast of Gallup can be a new experience in outdoor recreation. McGaffey Lake recreation area, not too far from the route of the *conquistadore* Juan de Oñate, is a cool retreat after crossing the desert and lava flow.

West of Socorro on U.S. Highway 60, with Magdalena as headquarters, the high Datil, Gallinas, and Magdalena mountains and another San Mateo range rise above the San Agustin Plains, an ancient lake bed. Mt. Withington and Mt. Baldy, 10,787 feet high, dominate the landscape. Good roads and developed campgrounds are available. Hunting for wild game as well as for unusual gem stones and geologic finds are favored activities in this western section of the Cibola. District ranger stations are at Grants, Gallup, Magdalena, Mountainair, and Tijeras.

LINCOLN NATIONAL FOREST

Named for the great president, the Lincoln National Forest, with headquarters at Alamogordo, has characteristics distinguishing it from all other National Forests in the state. The high mountains and canyons of the Sacramento, Guadalupe, Capitan, and White mountains, rising between the Tularosa and Pecos basins, were the backdrop and often the prize of the Indian and cattle wars. Stories and legends of early day happenings in the Tularosa Basin, mining operations, battles between rival cattle ranchers, large timber operations providing lumber, poles, mine props, and railroad ties are warp and woof of the Lincoln country. This Forest includes the high mountains north and south of the Mescalero Apache Indian Reservation.

During the last decade, the Lincoln National Forest gained new fame as the birthplace of the world-renowned Smokey the Bear, symbol of forest fire prevention. In the Capitan Mountains, travelers like to visit Smokey's birthplace near Capitan Pass, and in the community of Capitan on U.S. Highway 380 is a log museum which features the activities of the bear cub found near there during a disastrous fire.

For the outdoor enthusiast, the Forest offers superb beauty, graceful and majestic snow-covered peaks, and the peace and serenity of a forest sanctuary. Each year, thousands of visitors from the plains seek its cool refuge from desert heat in summer and its readily accessible sports area in the winter. Ten campgrounds with many picnicking and camping sites are provided. Canyons, mountains, and streams in many instances feature anglicized names—Big Dog Canyon, Mule Peak, Bug Scuffle Hill—though the influence of the early Spanish settler still remains in names such as Sacramento, Agua Chiquita, Ruidoso, and Rio Penasco.

Lincoln National Forest abounds in points of interest; Monjeau Lookout overlooks the headwaters of the Bonito, Eagle, and Ruidoso creeks as well as the tall slopes of Sierra Blanca to the southwest. Sierra Blanca, 12,003 feet high, is the most southerly mountain of that elevation in the continental United States. Just north of the peak is the Sierra Blanca Recreation Area, with one of the finest and best-equipped skiing facilities in the country. The restaurant and gondola lift operate during summer months, and from Lookout Mountain observation site, near the gondola's upper terminal, the traveler can view White Sands, the Malpais (lava flow), and the 28,000-acre White Mountain Wild Area.

Hunters find deer of three distinct types in this Forest—the Rocky Mountain mule deer, the desert mule deer, and the Texas white-tailed deer—and, of course, black bear from which family Smokey the Bear came. Game birds like wild turkey, quail, and chukkar partridge challenge the hunter. Fishing the Lincoln's lakes and streams is a recurring delight to the angler. Aspens and oaks flaunt their brilliant autumn coloring against the warm green of pines and spruces, heralding the advent of winter snows and provoking numerous aspencades for those who wish a share in this ever new pageant of nature's beauty.

Like all the National Forests, the Lincoln is managed for the production and wise use of water, timber, and forage for livestock and wildlife and outdoor recreation. District ranger stations are at Cloudcroft, Carlsbad, Mayhill, Ruidoso, Sacramento, and Capitan.

"Anybody for a run?" AT SIERRA BLANCA SKI AREA

GILA NATIONAL FOREST

The Gila National Forest, with headquarters in Silver City, is a big, wild, wonderful country in the southwestern section of the state. It has been scarcely affected by the hustle and bustle of modern living. Within its boundaries are 2.7 million acres of public-owned forest and range land, with almost a quarter of it devoted to wilderness and primitive areas. It includes the famous Gila Wilderness, the first such area set aside in the United States and the largest in the Southwest. Most of the Gila National Forest is north of Silver City, though part of it lies in the high country between Silver City and Lordsburg.

The Gila is an exciting and exhilarating place to explore, sightsee, hunt, fish, and just enjoy. Indian ruins are evident almost everywhere, but the Gila Cliff Dwellings National Monument, adjacent to the Gila Primitive Area, is the best preserved. Ancient tree stumps and abandoned Indian ruins record the history of man; old mine dumps contain ores and minerals not known nor appreciated in the heyday of local mining; microscopic plants and forest grasses which may hold the key to man's future health abound; and the traveler may experience great delight in finding a dried root or branch to add to a native rock garden; the majestic peaks, deer and other wild game, and cool, splashing waters of a mountain creek delight the camera hobbyist.

One of the most beautiful and spectacular box canyons in the Southwest is on Whitewater Creek about four miles northeast of Glenwood. A catwalk built against the rock walls of the canyon enables the traveler to thrill at the unusual beauty and colors of the canyon and the cool depths of the trout stream below (*see* Frontispiece).

Good roads lead into the Gila National Forest at Reserve and Alma from U.S. Highway 260. An enjoyable loop trip which touches the Gila Wilderness at Willow Creek can be taken on State Highway 78 from Alma. Another beautiful trip is through the Black Range from the junction of State Highway 180 and U.S. Highway 85 to Silver City. Approach to the Gila from the north can be made through Beaverhead, Apache Creek, and Reserve, where good roads lead into the Forest.

Fifteen developed recreation areas provide camping and picnicking for the hiker, horseback rider, and motorist and are complete with fireplaces, tables, and benches. Elk, deer, antelope, bear, javelina, and game birds are plentiful, and fishing in the high mountain creeks is usually rewarded with a satisfying catch.

District ranger stations are at Magdalena, Truth or Consequences, Reserve, Glenwood, and Mimbres.

APACHE AND CORONADO FORESTS

Although small parts of these forests lie in New Mexico, they belong to forests in Arizona. Apache National Forest touches the northern edge of the Gila and its attractions are much like those of the latter. The Coronado National Forest, which is in the extreme southwest corner of

101

New Mexico, lies in an area of aridity and is difficult to reach from New Mexico. It is surrounded by Sonoran desert, at least in its environment in this state.

These far-flung public lands in New Mexico provide many resources besides varied kinds of outdoor recreation: timber for industry, water for city and farm, forage for livestock and wildlife. As long as our National Forests are protected and developed—used but not abused—they will continue to yield rich harvests, both tangible and intangible, forever.

LAKE ROBERTS

This 70-acre lake thirty miles northeast of Silver City on State Highway 25 lies in the Gila National Forest.

The State Also Preserves*

State Monuments have been established to preserve some of New Mexico's historic and archeologic sites of importance. These include the mission ruins of Abo, Quarai, Pecos, and Jemez, the Palace of the Governors in Santa Fe, pueblo ruins at Coronado State Monument, the old Lincoln County Courthouse, the archeologic site at Folsom Man State Monument, the plaza and nearby Mexican Colonial-style buildings in La Mesilla, and Fort Selden. The history recorded at these sites dates from 10,000 B.C. of Clovis Man to 1878 of the cattlemen's Lincoln County War.

State parks cover areas of scenic beauty, geologic wonders, and historic interest. Reservoir lakes yielding necessary water, good fishing, swimming, and boating include Conchas, Storrie, Bluewater, El Vado, Ute, Elephant Butte, Caballo, Alamogordo, Clayton, Morphy, and Bottomless Lakes. The latter are natural sink holes east of Roswell. Hyde Memorial Park and Santa Fe River Park, near and in Santa Fe, provide scenic picnic spots, as do Rock Hound State Park near Deming and Oasis State Park near Portales and Clovis. Picnicking, fishing, and spectacular canyons attract the visitor at Rio Grande Gorge Park west of Taos. Weird erosional figures carved from volcanic layers distinguish City of Rocks State Park near Deming. Pancho Villa State Park at Columbus and Kit Carson Memorial at Taos mark historic sites. Valley of Fires State Park west of Carrizozo preserves the black twisted lava of a relatively recent volcanic flow.

NEW MEXICO STATE MONUMENTS
by MUSEUM OF NEW MEXICO STAFF

The State of New Mexico, recognizing the depth and color of its own history, has established a number of state monuments preserving important historical or archeological sites. These are administered by the Museum of New Mexico located in Santa Fe. Any mosaic of New Mexico would be incomplete without including these important landmarks.

EL PALACIO, PALACE OF THE GOVERNORS

The main facility of the Museum of New Mexico is El Palacio. The Palace of the Governors, on the plaza in the heart of Santa Fe, is the oldest public building in the United States. Built in 1610, it was the seat of Spanish government in New Mexico until 1821, of the Mexican government until 1846, and the residence of the governors appointed by the President of the United States until 1910, when it became a unit of the Museum of New Mexico.

It presently contains exhibits relating to New Mexico's past, ranging from the Indians, who arrived after crossing the Bering Sea, to the Spanish, who came seeking gold and glory on horseback, to the wagon trains from the east, whose goal was the end of the Santa Fe Trail, which is directly in front of El Palacio.

---

* Information on monuments and parks developed since this publication was first printed may be obtained from The New Mexico State Park and Recreation Commission, Sante Fe, New Mexico 87501.

El Palacio was the capitol of New Mexico for 300 years and was the seat of residence for more than one hundred of New Mexico's governors. During that time it was captured and held by the Indians from 1680 to 1692. The Army of the Confederacy captured it for a few days during the Civil War, and one of its occupants, Territorial Governor Lew. Wallace, wrote his famous novel, *Ben Hur*, within its walls.

There are other fascinating units connected with the Museum of New Mexico in Santa Fe. Among these are the Fine Arts Museum, emphasizing the art and artists of the great Southwest; the International Folk Art Museum; and the Hall of Ethnology, devoted primarily to the peoples of the Southwest.

ABO STATE MONUMENT

Off U.S. Highway 60, nine miles west of Mountainair is Abo State Monument.

The ruins of the ancient mission church of San Gregorio de Abo and its pueblo, built of red sandstone, are in a broad, natural amphitheater rimmed on the north and west by the blue Manzano Mountains, which contrast strikingly with the reddish hues of the Abo sandstone. This is one of the Saline Missions, so called because of the nearby salt deposits in the Estancia Basin.

It was built during the seventeenth century by Indians under the supervision of the Franciscans, led by the venerable Fray Francisco de Acevedo. The inhabitants of Abo were very friendly to the Spaniards. They were forced to abandon their pueblo about 1673 because of drought and the raids of the Apaches and Comanches. They then moved south to El Paso del Norte where they joined in founding Isleta del Sur.

The walls of the pueblo have disintegrated with time into low mounds which lie adjacent to the mission. The ecclesiastical structures have been excavated and repaired for permanent preservation.

QUARAI STATE MONUMENT

This monument is near Punta de Agua, eight miles north of Mountainair off State Highway 10.

The ruins of the mission church of the Immaculate Conception at Quarai are unsurpassed in grandeur of architecture or setting by any that survive from the labors of the early Franciscans in New Mexico. Built of red sandstone masonry about 1628, at the Pueblo of Quarai, it was abandoned along with the pueblo about 1674, chiefly because of Apache depredations.

One of the most venerated of the Franciscan missionaries, Fray Geronimo de la Llana, worked and died at Quarai, beloved by his Indian charges. His remains now rest in a crypt in the wall of St. Francis Cathedral in Santa Fe. The ruins have been excavated and repaired for permanent preservation.

CORONADO STATE MONUMENT

This pueblo ruin is on the west bank of the Rio Grande, one mile from the town of Bernalillo, seventeen miles north of Albuquerque, and one mile off U.S. Highway 85, between Albuquerque and Santa Fe.

The Pueblo of Kuaua was one of the several towns of the ancient Tiguex province. At or near Kuaua, the Coronado expedition maintained headquarters from about 1540 to 1542 A.D. During excavation of the ancient pueblo, more than 1200 ground-floor rooms were found and five kivas, or underground ceremonial chambers, were uncovered.

In one of the kivas was found a highly important group of ancient wall paintings. This kiva has been reconstructed and the paintings restored.

The old walls of Kuaua have been rebuilt to a few feet in height so that the structure can be seen. A museum has been erected on the site to exhibit the material found during the excavation and to portray life in the Tiguex province. The Coronado State Monument and Museum commemorates the meeting, more than four hundred years ago, of the elements that influenced the culture of New Mexico—the Indian and the *conquistadore*.

A curator-custodian is on duty at the Coronado Museum headquarters, which is open all year.

PECOS STATE MONUMENT

Off U.S. Highway 84-85, three miles south of Pecos, is this State Monument. It became a National Monument during late 1966.

This mission, the Church of Nuestra Senora de los Angeles de Porciuncula at Pecos, dates from the year 1617. It is fitting that this mission, which was one of the first two, with Jemez, established by the Franciscans in New Mexico, should bear the name "Our Lady of the Angels of Porciuncula," for with his own hands, St. Francis, founder of the Order, rebuilt the decaying chapel of Our Lady of Angels at Assisi, which he called his Porciuncula or "Little Inheritance," and there established the headquarters of the Franciscan Order.

Pecos was well fortified because of its location on the eastern edge of the pueblo area and its contact with the Plains Indians. It resisted the raids for many years, but when a smallpox epidemic in 1838 reduced the population to seventeen survivors, they moved to Jemez Pueblo, adandoning Pecos.

A part of the massive adobe walls of the ruined mission has been excavated and repaired, as have some of the rubble masonry walls.

JEMEZ STATE MONUMENT

This Monument is at Jemez Springs, sixty miles north of Albuquerque on State Highway 4.

One of the finest early mission churches was established at Giusewa Pueblo. *Giusewa* means "place of the boiling waters" in the language of the Jemez Indians, and refers to the famous Jemez Hot Springs nearby. The mission, with Pecos, was one of the two earliest in New Mexico. These were founded one hundred and fifty-two years before the first California missions.

The original settlement of the Giusewa Pueblo goes back hundreds of years before Columbus' discovery of America, as does the settlement of the other pueblos, Quarai, Abo, and Pecos.

Guisewa Pueblo became extinct during the last quarter of the seventeenth century, a result of the consolidation of several pueblos of the Jemez province into fewer and larger towns. Only one town, the present Jemez Pueblo, survives from that time. Excavation and repairs have been made in the ruins of both the pueblo and the mission church.

LA MESILLA STATE MONUMENT

This colorful State Monument consists of the plaza in the village of Mesilla, near Las Cruces, and the buildings nearby. The Monument preserves an aspect of the Mexican Colonial culture and architecture which flourished here in the early nineteenth century. The Gadsden Purchase of 1853 was celebrated in the Mesilla Plaza and the famous desperado, Billy the Kid, once stood trial here for his life. During the Civil War, Mesilla was briefly the Confederate capitol of the Territory of Arizona.

LINCOLN STATE MONUMENT

Located in Lincoln, on U.S. Highway 380, and known as the Old Lincoln County Courthouse, the first floor of this Monument was the mercantile store of L. G. Murphy & Co. in the 1870's, during the Lincoln County War. The second floor was purchased in 1870 by the county for a court house.

It was from this building that Billy the Kid made his daring escape on April 28, 1881, after killing his two guards. A caretaker and a museum attendant are on duty at all times. Mementos of the infamous Lincoln County cattle war are featured.

FORT SELDEN STATE MONUMENT

The crumbling adobe walls of Fort Selden lie about seventeen miles north of Las Cruces just west of Interstate Highway 25. The history of this fort, given in the article on *Frontier Forts,* was highlighted by the brief stay of General Douglas MacArthur, who spent some of his childhood within the fort's walls and played in the adjoining green valley of the Rio Grande.

NEW MEXICO STATE PARKS
by THE EDITORS

New Mexico is blessed with a wealth of natural resources and perhaps most important is the abundance of sites with outstanding scenic and recreational facilities. The contrasts apparent in the mosaic of New Mexico are also seen in the pattern of its state parks. They range from desert regions with sparse and exotic flora and fauna to the high mountain canyons choked with Douglas fir and aspen where even in the summer evenings one huddles close to the fire for warmth. And the mosaic shifts from waterless areas amid geologic wonders to wide expanses of open water well stocked with trout. The parks are administered by the New Mexico State Park and Recreation Commission. Wherever possible, areas have been set aside for the permanent enjoyment of the people of New Mexico and their visitors.

Bottomless Lakes State Park

Bottomless Lakes State Park, established in 1936, was one of the first of the New Mexico state parks. It is surprising to find this treasure of great natural beauty in an area so dominated by aridity. There are six small lakes in the park, of which Lea Lake is the largest with about 15 acres of surface area. The water of the lakes is crystal clear and varies in depth from 45 feet in the shallow lakes to about 100 feet in the deeper ones. They were created as "sink holes" when water dissolved large areas of underground gypsum, resulting in cave-ins. The lakes now offer extensive recreational facilities for the people of New Mexico and for tourists passing through or visiting the area. Camping, swimming, and boating are available. Pecos "diamonds," small quartz crystals, can be found in the neighboring hills.

Conchas Lake State Park

Conchas Lake is one of the largest sustained bodies of water in New Mexico. Conchas Dam, which holds the water of the Canadian River, forms the lake. The main dam is 235 feet above the roadway and is 1250 feet in length. At capacity it holds 600,000 acre-feet of water. The reservoir

SKETCH OF BOTTOMLESS LAKE

serves many purposes: flood control, local irrigation, camping and boating facilities, and fishing and water skiing.

The Canadian River has its origin on Raton Mesa and flows southward to Conchas Dam, then turns abruptly eastward. On its way across the High Plains, it cuts into some of the oldest rocks that can be seen on the western edge of the plains, the Dockum Group of Late Triassic age. The best place to view the earth-building processes of this region is where State Highway 120 crosses the gorge of the Canadian River between Wagon Mound and Roy.

HYDE MEMORIAL STATE PARK

Here, at an elevation of 9000 feet, among tall pines and aspens is one of the most scenic of all New Mexico's parks. High in the Sangre de Cristo Mountains, eight miles northeast of Santa Fe, the park offers an excellent example of the scenic beauty in New Mexico rarely seen by most travelers passing through the state. Easily accessible from Santa Fe, Hyde Park gives a few moments, or a few days, respite in the cool refreshment of a mountain forest. Excellent picnic and camping facilities are available. For those who want to penetrate the mountain vastness even farther, there are a number of well-marked trails for hiking.

NAVAJO LAKE STATE PARK

Navajo Dam on the San Juan River lies twenty-five miles east of Aztec at an elevation of 6200 feet in a region of spectacular scenic beauty. Camping, picnicking, boating, fishing, and water skiing facilities are available, and a lodge is under construction. This is expected to be one of the most important sports and recreational centers in northwest New Mexico in coming years.

PANCHO VILLA STATE PARK

Named for the famous Mexican bandit and revolutionary leader, the park is located near Columbus, New Mexico, site of Villa's most infamous raid. In the dead of the night on March 10, 1916, Villa and his men entered the town of Columbus and did their bloody work. When they left, seventeen local people were dead, including eight soldiers and nine civilians. The Mexican force suffered heavy casualties, perhaps as many as 125 killed. The town of Columbus was badly damaged and has only recently begun to recover from the blow. The expedition of General Pershing, then on duty along the Mexican border, was organized to hunt down Villa and his men. Pershing and a United States military unit spent three months inside Mexico, only to return to the United States empty-handed. The park commemorates one of the most interesting and tragic episodes in New Mexico history. Within the park, one can see excellent examples of Sonoran desert flora. Picnic facilities and camping sites are available.

EL VADO LAKE STATE PARK

El Vado Dam is a part of the complex Rio Grande Conservancy District flood and irrigation project. It holds the water of the Chama River, which flows west, south, and then east into the Rio Grande. The country surrounding El Vado Lake is beautiful and contains some of the finest trout fishing streams in the state. At the lake itself there are camping facilities, including trailer spaces (no hookups for water or electricity). The lake is at an elevation of 7000 feet and is one of the important flood-control bodies of water in New Mexico.

BLUEWATER STATE PARK

Bluewater Lake, at an elevation of 7460 feet, is a spot of spectacular beauty. Adjacent is a 160-acre wooded park. The area offers boating, fishing, and swimming. The lake was formed by impounding the waters from the Zuni Mountains' watershed, and it fills three great depressions in high tablelands. The dam, built across two lofty natural walls of solid rock, the San Andres Limestone, holds a lake a mile wide and seven and a half miles long. Bluewater Lake State Park was the first of New Mexico's parks, so designated in 1929.

STORRIE LAKE STATE PARK

Storrie Lake State Park surrounds a small lake north of Las Vegas, New Mexico. It lies on the west edge of the High Plains and is an excellent recreation area. The lake is at an elevation of 6400 feet and has a limited number of picnic and camping facilities. It is stocked with rainbow and brown trout and crappies.

CITY OF ROCKS STATE PARK

This is one of the most unusual of the state parks, and one of the finest for picnicking and for camping. Located in the unusual rock formation known as the Sugarlump Welded Rhyolite Tuff northwest of Deming, it is a source of wonder to all visitors. Suddenly, in a seemingly flat, desert plain, one comes upon these grotesque outcrops. In the coolness of the shade of these ancient rocks one can survey vistas under an azure sky that are almost breathless. This is the desert Southwest at its very best; not the harsh, unfriendly desert of movies and fiction, but a lovely spot in which to enjoy to the fullest the wonders of nature.

KIT CARSON MEMORIAL PARK

This 20-acre plot of grass, flower beds, trees, and picnic tables lies on the northeast edge of Taos and contains the graves of Kit Carson and Padre José Martinez. Not far away is the Kit Carson House, a group of adobe buildings surrounding a patio, that was Carson's headquarters, office, and home from 1858 to 1866. This Indian fighter, trapper, hunter, and trader is most famous for defeating the Navajos in Canyon de Chelly and marching 7000 of these Indians across New Mexico to a reservation at

Bosque Redondo near Fort Sumner. However, during his eight
Indian agent, Carson worked continuously for the welfare of his ⟨

OASIS STATE PARK

One of the state's newest parks, Oasis is seven miles northeast of
tales along State Highway 467. This shady place of cottonwood trees ⟨
sand dunes has long been a favorite picnic spot. The sand dunes form ⟨⟨⟨
irregular ridge separating Portales Valley to the south from Blackwater
Draw to the north. In Blackwater Draw have been found bones of ancient
animals and the weapons used by early man some 12,000 years ago. Portales Valley is the sand-filled remnant of the early Pleistocene Brazos
River Valley that once drained eastward into Texas. About 800,000 years
ago, the Pecos River to the west "captured" the headwaters of this former
Brazos River and left the Portales Valley high and dry.

VALLEY OF FIRES STATE PARK

This park, about five miles west of Carrizozo on U.S. Highway 380,
features picnic tables amid the Carrizozo lava flow, or malpais, one of the
youngest in the United States. The lava flowed out of Little Black Peak
about 1000 years ago in a series of individual "rivers" of hot black basalt.
The composite flow is 44 miles long, 0.5 to 6 miles wide, and is made up
of about 1 cubic mile of basalt; it moved southward down the lowest part
of the northern Tularosa Basin.

Climb around on the lava and note the ropy nature of the surface
(*pahoehoe* of the Hawaiians), the many frozen gas bubbles in the rocks
(vesicles), the squeeze-ups where once-liquid lava protrudes through cracks
in the hardened crust, the pressure ridges where the hardened crust arched
and broke, and collapsed lava tunnels where the outer lava froze and the
molten interior ran out, leaving an open tube or cave.

UTE LAKE STATE PARK

Ute Dam, two miles southwest of Logan, provides a 4200-acre reservoir
along the Canadian River and Ute Creek stocked with rainbow trout, bass,
crappie, and catfish. Camping, picnicking, and boating facilities are available along the valley walls, which are cut in the brown Santa Rosa Sandstone and overlying maroon to green Chinle shales.

SANTA FE RIVER STATE PARK

Bordering the Santa Fe River in downtown Santa Fe, this city park
merges with the State Capitol grounds. It provides picnic tables and
benches in the shade of tall trees amid the picturesque ancient city.

ELEPHANT BUTTE LAKE STATE PARK

The giant Elephant Butte Reservoir, impounded behind the dam five
miles east of Truth or Consequences, provides year-around fishing, boating,
water skiing, and camping. Built in brown to gray Cretaceous sandstone
and shale, the dam is overlooked by the brownish-black volcanic neck that

is Elephant Butte. Eastern shores are carved from the purplish and maroon McRae layers. This is the main storage reservoir for the water that irrigates the lush Rio Grande Valley to the south near Las Cruces and El Paso.

CABALLO LAKE STATE PARK

Caballo Reservoir, downstream from Elephant Butte, offers excellent facilities for water sports, its bass and crappie fishing being notable. The State Park is fourteen miles south of Truth or Consequences and six miles north of the dam. The spectacular rugged front of the Caballo Mountains looms to the east, with sharp canyons and ribbed cliffs along the valley walls cut in the tan layers of the Santa Fe Formation.

RIO GRANDE GORGE STATE PARK

From Velarde (twelve miles north of Espanola) for seventy miles northward to the Colorado state line, the Rio Grande Gorge is carved 500 to 800 feet into black basalt flows and tan Santa Fe Formation layers. Fishing is exciting in the fast waters, although the northern part of the gorge is difficult to reach. Foot and horseback trails lead to the bottom at the mouth of Red River west of Questa where picnic units have been built.

ALAMOGORDO LAKE STATE PARK

The dam of Alamogordo Reservoir blocks the Pecos River and Alamogordo Creek northwest of Fort Sumner. Picnic, camp, and water sports facilities lie along U.S. Highway 84 about sixteen miles northwest of Fort Sumner. Juniper trees dot the low valley walls where the maroon to green shale and sandstone of the Chinle Formation crop out.

ROCK HOUND STATE PARK

Lying on the west flank of the Little Florida Mountains, Rock Hound State Park, twelve miles southeast of Deming, offers camping and picnicking facilities and many varieties of agate in the volcanic rocks. A few miles to the south tower cliffs of the Florida Mountains, a landmark of southwestern New Mexico and also happy hunting grounds for rock hounds.

CLAYTON LAKE STATE PARK

Serving the northeast corner of New Mexico, Clayton Lake State Park lies twelve miles north of Clayton on State Highway 370, impounded by a dam across Cieneguilla Creek. The stream bed cuts brown Dakota Sandstone, and rolling grassy hills to the south overlie weathered basalt flows.

MORPHY LAKE STATE PARK

Morphy Lake, backed up from a dam across Rito Morphy, lies three miles west of Ledoux in southwestern Mora County and thirty-one miles north of Las Vegas off State Highway 94. The 15-acre lake provides fine trout fishing and picnicking amid stately ponderosa pines, with the canyon walls formed by tier upon tier of Pennsylvanian limestones.

Angling in the Desert's Waters

by Fred A. Thompson*

Water in the great Southwest, of which the State of New Mexico is a part, has made for a colorful and historical background. Water, perhaps more than anything else, has molded the lives of all inhabitants of the area from the pueblo and lodge of the early Indian to the civilization we know today. The fish and wildlife resources as related to water have played an important part in everyday living and economy.

From data gathered by archeologists there are indications that the early Indian used fish as part of his diet. Fish bones are found in excavated ruins, and fish pictures are occasionally found as petroglyphs and on pottery (fig. 1). Although the use of fish was limited, it was widespread throughout the Southwest, not being confined to one Indian tribe or nation.

Figure 1. Bowl depicting fish, found in ruins of Mimbres Indians

* New Mexico Department of Game and Fish.

The use of fish by the white settler was likewise restricted, but it increased as time progressed and knowledge and equipment improved. There is only limited reference to fish for either food or sport fishing until after the middle of the nineteenth century. Early explorers made records of fish in various waters of New Mexico and in most instances described the new species.

Originally, the waters of the desert also could be described as fish deserts. Only three recognized kinds of food fish, as we know them today, inhabited the waters of this region. The trout was limited to the cutthroat species or subspecies. These were found as one subspecies in the Rio Grande drainage and the other subspecies in the Arkansas River drainage. The latter is reduced in numbers but a few remnants remain in the headwaters. The former is being artificially propagated and is being maintained successfully. The trout found in the Gila River drainage, originally thought to be a cutthroat, then a rainbow, has been recently described as a separate species. These trout, like the Arkansas River fish, remain as remnants in the headwaters. For the most part, the native trout have had a difficult time surviving in recent years because of the change in water and land use; the habitat has become exceedingly restricted.

Channel catfish were originally found in the Rio Grande drainage and continue to maintain themselves satisfactorily. Water and land manipulation, however, present a serious threat, even to this hardy fish.

There are records that the gulf eel once came up the Rio Grande during part of its life cycle. This fish of the ocean has long since disappeared—the fate of many migrating fish when confronted with man-made obstructions in the watercourses.

Waterfowl were in great abundance once, in both the upper Rio Grande and the Pecos River drainages. These birds utilized the vast marsh areas of the valleys during spring and fall migrations. It is presumed that there was very little nesting of waterfowl in the early years.

The mammals that live in or near the water, principally fur bearers, were in abundance as long as water habitat was abundant and prior to unrestricted trapping. With the exception of the beaver (since restocked and protected), many of the fur bearers once numerous are now extremely limited in numbers or approaching extinction. There is only an occasional sighting of the otter which was once relatively plentiful.

Habitat for the various water mammals, birds, and fish is found in the drainage systems. The major system is the Rio Grande that flows through the center of the state; the Pecos River is its tributary. In this system are six of the seven life zones and conditions of habitat suitable to almost any form of water-dwelling life.

There is a noticeable habitat change due to several causes, such as ranching, irrigation, urban development, and a general minor change in climatic conditions. Many variations are in direct relation, such as improper grazing, unscreened irrigation diversions, dams, and sewage disposal, to mention a few. There is an indication of a long-term warming

114

of the general Southwest, and though this change is fractional, it does have a basic effect on habitat.

The effect of habitat change can be noted in the life of the cutthroat trout. Early records reveal that this trout, liking cool clear water, was once caught in the Rio Grande in the lower part of the box canyon north of Peñablanca. It was also caught near the town of Pecos. The fish can no longer survive in the changed water conditions and is found now only in the headwaters. Even the catfish has difficulty surviving in some sections of the rivers for lack of water. In the lower Pecos, the catfish finds difficulty in reproducing because of the high salt content of the river water.

As has already been noted, the fish that are recognized as game fish today were in short supply a hundred years ago. It was not until the railroads entered New Mexico that fish were imported to supplement the native supply. In an unpublished report by the author, it was pointed out that almost every kind of fish propagated in the United States has been imported and stocked in waters of New Mexico. Of these, some have survived beyond expectations and others have disappeared entirely.

When the railroads entered New Mexico, there were already requests for fish in the hands of the United States Fish Commission. Fish were delivered in especially designed fish-distribution cars and the consignee met the cars at designated rail sidings. From the distribution cars, the fish were further transported by wagons in water containers of various descriptions, usually wooden barrels or watertight wooden boxes, to streams or lakes as assigned. Because of the mode of travel at the time, the quantities of fish so stocked were limited, but they did provide seed stock from which their population could grow. Fish were packed on back and on horses into relatively inaccessible areas. The procedures and techniques of fish transportation have evolved to the present highly specialized equipment and methods of operation.

It is interesting to note that the quantities of fish imported and planted increased in relation to the improved transportation. The early records indicate the numbers in the hundreds and in just a few locations; later plantings increased both in numbers stocked and in waters stocked. The first fish imported to supplement the native fish was the German carp. In fact, this was the only fish imported for eight consecutive years, 1883-1890. These early plantings were followed by catfish, German brown trout, brook trout, yellow perch, largemouth black bass, crappie, rock bass, tench, rainbow trout, strawberry bass, black spotted trout, bream, smallmouth bass, salmon, white bass, and walleyed pike.

All the fish imported are classed as game fish except carp and tench (the latter did not survive). The various species met their habitat requirements, and although there were no survivals in some locations, they did acclimate in others and have developed into a substantial fishery. Some species are predominant while others, like the rock bass, are remnant and taken only occasionally. The fish most sought now and predominant in the fishery are rainbow (fig. 2) and brown trout, catfish, largemouth bass, crappie, and walleyed pike.

Figure 2. JOY OF THE FISHERMAN, RAINBOW TROUT

Management of the fishery has progressed with technical development. When fish were planted in early years, very little thought was given about the habitat except that it was water. There was little known of the requirements of fish. As a result, fish were placed in waters only to perish. To maintain a fish population now, all techniques available are employed and fish are stocked where water and species are compatible.

Water in the desert is always at a premium for the inhabitants. The early Indian cultures used water for irrigation, and there are still vestiges of canals used by Indians to convey water to their crops. The use of water by the Indians then had little or no effect on fish life, but as irrigation development increased, a new habitat was formed. The once free-flowing

116

rivers became dry in places, and new waters were developed in the drainage ditches in the Rio Grande Valley. The competition for water is very keen and fish and wildlife uses come after domestic, commerical, and irrigation purposes.

The water requirements are so great, in fact, that it has been necessary to control water and its use by laws. The law of 1876 provided that water could not be refused a traveler. Community ditch commissioners were established by law in 1895. The basic laws governing water rights were established in 1907. These laws have been amended or added to as conditions dictate. Conservancy districts were recognized by law in 1927, and underground waters came under law in 1931. The Interstate Stream Commission was created in 1935. At present, New Mexico water laws are considered some of the best in the nation; however, it has been only recently that water for fish and wildlife has been recognized as one of the beneficial uses.

Converse to the use of water to the detriment of fish and wildlife, there are several areas in which water has been developed and impounded to the benefit of the fishery. Although some impoundments were single-purpose developments, they supply habitat in conservation pools or during years of abundant water supply.

Waters impounded by man but used as a fishery are Elephant Butte Reservoir (fig. 3), 40,096 surface acres when full. It contains largemouth black bass, crappie, walleyed pike, catfish, and sunfish. This lake has not been full for many years; but like Alamogordo Reservoir (4650 surface acres), Caballo Reservoir (11,532 surface acres), McMillan Reservoir

Figure 3. FIND THE ELEPHANT!—AT ELEPHANT BUTTE RESERVOIR

(2500 surface acres), Conchas Reservoir (16,640 surface acres), and Avalon Reservoir (950 surface acres), it has produced excellent fishing. These are large irrigation lakes and are all stocked generally with the same species of fish.

The lakes built for irrigation but utilized for trout are usually much smaller. The principal ones are Navajo Reservoir (15,600 surface acres) and El Vado (3500 surface acres). There are also Miami Lake (190 surface acres) and several others of small size.

In addition, several small lakes have been built or acquired for the primary purpose of providing fishing. A few of these are Hopewell Lake (14 surface acres), Lake Roberts (73 surface acres), and Charette Lakes (400 surface acres). There are many more varying in size. The smaller lakes are primarily for trout fishing, but a few in the southern part of the state do have species usually found in warmer waters.

In the process of reservoir construction, waterfowl habitat and resting areas are created. These new lakes, however, are a poor substitute for the natural marshes and potholes originally frequented by ducks and geese. Water mammals, likewise, find the artificial impoundments undesirable in comparison, and the increased water has added very little to this resource.

Every water development has with it the appeal of recreation other than fishing. Now a lake must have such facilities as picnic and camping areas, launching ramps, good accessibility, boat rentals, and a concessionaire. There is no single-purpose reservoir in respect to recreation.

Finally, it is concluded that the old adage, "fishing ain't what it used to be," should no longer be true for New Mexico. The fishing water has been added to greatly and the fish are managed better. The only problem is one of increased human population. Where there was one fisherman fifty years ago, there are a thousand now.

Truly, the water of the desert is used to the limit.

THE PAST LIVING TODAY—SAN MIGUEL, EARLY MISSION CHURCH STILL
USED DAILY IN SANTA FE

119

The Indians of New Mexico

by Paige W. Christiansen

People entering New Mexico today find Indian cultures and Indian villages with traditions and ways of life that have changed little in many centuries. In this respect, man in the twentieth century shares an experience in common with Coronado, Oñate, and all the other *conquistadores* who visited New Mexico so many generations ago. They, too, found the ancient Indian cultures strangely magnetic and exciting. If we could but remove the asphalt highways, the billboards, the telephone poles, and fences that seem always to surround us, the Indian villages in many parts of the state would look very much as they looked to the early Spanish explorers who were the first Europeans to see them. To meet the Indians of New Mexico and to visit their homes, if possible, is one of the greatest experiences available to residents and visitors alike. Although words are inadequate to give the true flavor and excitement of the Indian and his way of life, they are all we have to introduce the various people who make up the Indian population of New Mexico.

There are two main groups that should be known. First, the Pueblo Indians, those who developed sedentary village life and who are the descendants of the first Americans in New Mexico. Second, the "newcomers" to the state, those who, for some reason or other, moved into the state to replace earlier cultures. Let us, then, visit some of these people's homes.

ACOMA PUEBLO

Acoma Indian Pueblo, the Sky City, is famous in both history and legend. Built on the top of a lofty, almost inaccessible, redrock mesa some 357 feet high, it is one of the most picturesque of all New Mexico Indian pueblos. No other pueblo gives one such a clear sense of living in ancestral times. The movements of the people up and down the steep trails, the untiring vistas, and the ancient homesites are reminiscent of the life and times of the cliff dwellers. Here the archeologists can search out the secrets of ancient life by direct observation. Here, too, is brought forth in the fullness of its bloom an Indian culture of outstanding achievement.

The Indians of Acoma participated in the great Pueblo Revolt of 1680. They killed their priest, Fray Lucas Maldonado, in the first frenzy of the rebellion. Because of their isolation and the inaccessibility of the village, they were spared the vengeance of the Spaniards under de Vargas during the reconquest in 1692. There was an attempt by the Spanish in 1696 to take Acoma, but they succeeded only in destroying the crops and in capturing five Acoma warriors. The Indians held out until July 6, 1699, when they submitted to the Spanish governor of New Mexico, Gov-

(Forest Service, U.S.D.A., by Starr Jenkins)

ASPEN BASIN IN SANGRE DE CRISTO MOUNTAINS NEAR SANTA FE

(Forest Service, U.S.D.A., by John Whiteside)

TENT ROCKS IN JEMEZ MOUNTAINS

ernor Cubero. Thereafter, Acoma became an integral part of the mission complex established in New Mexico by the Spanish.

Acoma is noted for its excellent pottery. The ware is fashioned from clay of fine quality, is very well fired, and is carefully decorated in typical Acoma designs. Here is an excellent example of Indian artistic ability. Some weaving, such as belts and headbands, is engaged in and a few baskets are produced, but Acoma is most famous for its pottery.

One of the landmarks at Acoma is the great church which brave Fray Juan Ramirez toiled to create in the early seventeenth century. Surely there are few memorials of the Spanish epoch in the Southwest that present such a picture of dauntless faith in spiritual ideals as does this fortress church silhouetted high against the sky above the bare-rock mesa. It measures 150 feet in length and has walls that are 60 feet high and 10 feet thick. Timbers 40 feet long and 14 inches through support the roof and make a handsome ceiling. There are, of course, no seats and little decoration. And what a location for so magnificent a spiritual center it is! From there one may lift his eyes in rapt admiration of the splendid panorama of the great plain and the encircling mountains, and thereby appreciate more fully the work of the Deity.

The Acoma are agriculturists, cultivating their lands by irrigation; they raise corn, wheat, melons, squashes, and hay. Now, however, most of the people of Acoma do not live on their mesa which protected them for so many centuries. The dangers of attack are no longer present, and the farmers find it more advantageous to live closer to their irrigated plots. The result is that the people of Acoma are now scattered throughout several villages. Their great culture, their traditions, their fierce pride, and their deep reverence for their spectacular history is visible in their faces and manners. Acoma, the Sky City, remains the eternal city of New Mexico.

COCHITI PUEBLO

The Indians of Cochiti Pueblo claim the famed cave dwellings and ruins of the Rito de Frijoles (Bandelier National Monument) as their ancestral home. Failure of timber and water resources plus the constant attack of the various Apache Indian tribes over several centuries caused the residents of the Rito de Frijoles to seek a better home. This probably occurred about 1200 A.D. In 1598, when Juan de Oñate, colonizer of New Mexico, arrived, the Indians of Cochiti were living in their present village. For a short time following the reconquest of New Mexico by de Vargas after the Pueblo Revolt, the people of Cochiti lived in Cañada de Cochiti, which was in a better position for defense against Spanish reconquest. In 1694, de Vargas took the canyon village by storm, burned it, and forced the people to return to the older village of Cochiti where they remain to this day.

The population of the village is slightly more than 300, and there has been little growth in the past thirty years. Like the other New Mexico pueblos, the main occupation is agriculture. Their ancient traditions are

122

well preserved, among them the well-known Rain Dance held during the annual festival of San Buenaventura in July.

Located at the pueblo is the ancient and beautiful Spanish mission, San Buenaventura de Cochiti, built in the early seventeenth century. To step into this church is to return to the Spanish days of yore. There are no seats, women kneel on one side, the men on the other, and the services are a mixture of old world orthodoxy and new world Indian traditions. Cochiti represents one of the finest examples of modern Pueblo Indian life.

ISLETA PUEBLO

Isleta Pueblo is the southernmost of the pueblos lying along the green and lush Rio Grande Valley today. It stands on the same site it occupied when Coronado came in 1540 and was a stopping place for every Spanish explorer and traveler who passed through New Mexico. It did not take part in the Pueblo Revolt of 1680, but rather joined the Spanish in the retreat to El Paso del Norte (modern Juarez, Mexico). There they founded a new village just to the south of modern El Paso which they called Isleta del Sur. The main village of Isleta, in New Mexico, remained deserted until 1709 when it was re-established by Fray Juan de la Peña.

Two different missions were built at Isleta Pueblo. The first, San Antonio de Isleta, was constructed about 1629. The church was burned in 1680, and in 1681 was being used as a sheep corral. Between 1680 and the completion of the reconquest, it was completely destroyed. The second mission, still remaining at Isleta, called San Agustin de Isleta, was built in 1709 on the old site.

Agriculture is the primary pursuit of the Indians of Isleta, although they do considerable stock grazing. The population of Isleta is nearly 2000 persons. The annual fiesta takes place in late August.

JEMEZ PUEBLO

The Jemez Indians were first seen by Europeans in 1541 when they were visited by Captain Francisco de Barrio-Nuevo, of Coronado's expedition. He counted seven villages, naming them Aguas Calientes because of the many hot springs in the canyon of the Jemez River. The ancient pueblos are now all in ruins, with one preserved as the Jemez State Monument. The present pueblo, built on the mesa where the Jemez River leaves the mountains, was constructed after the Pueblo Revolt. The Jemez people fled their older villages during the reconquest and for a time lived with the Navajo, whom they disliked but preferred to the Spanish.

There have been four notable missions among the Jemez Indians. The first, San Diego de Jemez Mission, was built in the early seventeenth century. It was one of the most successful of the New Mexico missions; reportedly, more than 6000 converts were made among the Jemez Indians before 1622. Because of the constant attacks of the Navajo, the traditional enemies of the Jemez people, the ancient pueblos gradually declined and were finally completely abandoned after Jemez participation in the Pueblo Revolt. The ruins of this church, now the Jemez State Monument, are among the most picturesque in all New Mexico. Its walls are three feet thick and were put together with intricate care. In its time, it must have been a beautiful building.

The second, San Juan de Los Jemez Mission, was built in 1617 at a village located near the junction of the Guadalupe and Jemez rivers, six miles north of the present pueblo. The ruins are faint but still visible. The mission was abandoned in 1680.

The third mission had a very brief history. It was called San Jose de los Jemez Mission and was located near San Juan de Los Jemez, of which it was a *visita*. Like San Juan, San Jose was abandoned in 1680.

The present mission was founded early in the eighteenth century and is one of the interesting things to visit at Jemez Pueblo. This old church is the center of the annual festival held at Jemez on November 12.

Jemez is noted for its splendid presentation of the Buffalo Dance in the winter and for its Corn Dances during the November festival.

Laguna Pueblo

Laguna Pueblo is the youngest and second largest of the pueblos in New Mexico. Built in 1697, shortly after the reconquest by de Vargas, the name was derived from a large lake which existed at one time just west of the village. In addition to the main village, a number of small settlements have developed where the terrain is suitable for agriculture, the main occupation of the Lagunas. The most important of these villages are Paguate, Encinal, Paraje, Mesita, Seama, and Casa Blanca. The Laguna Indians are of mixed origin, composed of four linguistic stocks: Tano, Keres, Shoshone, and Zuni.

Rock-walled Santa Maria mission, Laguna Reservation

Although the occupation of the pueblo was traditionally agriculture, in recent years a moderate revolution has been visible. The people of Laguna are in the middle of one of the richest uranium mining areas in the world, and many of them have been employed in mining activities. Also, the pueblo lies on the main line of the Santa Fe Railway, allowing some employment with the railroad. Laguna Pueblo is one of the most progressive of all the Indian groups in New Mexico. It has a population well in excess of 3000.

Located at Laguna is the San Jose de Laguna mission, built in 1699. The plaster on the building is native earth. Indian symbols are painted on the ceiling of the chancel, and a large picture of St. Joseph done on elk skin hangs on the reredos. The halos on the saints are triangular rather than circular. The altar is covered with animal skins painted with Christian symbols.

NAMBÉ PUEBLO

Nambé is one of the smallest of the pueblos but is located in an area noted for its scenic beauty and climate. Its population is less than 200. It was not always so small; during the eighteenth and nineteenth centuries, the population was greatly reduced by intertribal war and witchcraft executions. The Nambé people played an active role in the pueblo rebellion of 1680, murdering their priest and destroying their church.

The original church at Nambé was one of the first missions founded after the establishment of the first European settlement of San Gabriel at San Juan in 1598. Destroyed in 1680, it was rebuilt in 1696. In 1729, the converts had increased to such numbers that a new church was required. This church remained in use until 1909 when, because of carelessness in keeping it in repair, the roof collapsed during a storm. The annual Nambé fiesta is held in early October.

PICURÍS PUEBLO

Picurís is seldom visited by the tourist, for it lies in the mountains forty miles north of Santa Fe and can only be reached over a gravel road. The people of Picurís were among the most warlike of the normally peaceful pueblo peoples. They participated actively in the pueblo rebellion in 1680, killing their priest and all the Spaniards in the vicinity. They also participated in the battle for Santa Fe which broke Spanish power in New Mexico until 1692. After the revolt, fear of the Spanish caused them to abandon their village until they were induced to return in 1706. The population of Picurís is very small, being slightly more than 100.

One of the few old missions left in New Mexico, the San Lorenzo de Picurís church shows the strange mixture of Spanish and Indian traditions. Near the door is a human skull covered with an old cloth, but unfortunately, its story is lost to antiquity.

An interesting feature at Picurís is the unusual construction seen in some of the buildings. Made of puddled adobe, they are the oldest still standing of any pueblo in the Rio Grande Valley. The buildings were

125

made by pouring adobe mud into wall forms. This is the same kind of construction that is found at Casa Grande, Arizona, one of the significant prehistoric ruins in the United States.

POJOAQUE PUEBLO

Pojoaque, though still listed among the Indian villages of New Mexico, is no longer populated by Indians. Two missions were established at Pojoaque in the early Spanish days, the first shortly after 1600. This was destroyed in the rebellion in 1680. Later, in 1706, a new church was constructed which is still in use. The Indian population of Pojoaque was gradually reduced until, in 1900, the few remaining families abandoned the village. Since that time, Spanish-American families have occupied the buildings. It is a picturesque village seldom seen, for it is hidden from the passing tourist by a hill. Yet some of the buildings in this ancient village date back to pre-Coronado times and are a significant part of the romance of New Mexico.

SANDIA PUEBLO

Sandia Pueblo is a remnant of the Tiguex villages visited by Coronado in 1540. A mission was created at Sandia shortly after the colonization by Oñate, and it was an important mission center until the Pueblo Revolt. After the revolt, Sandia peoples scattered rather than again submit to Spanish control. Many of them went to live with the Hopi and there founded the village of Payupki on the middle mesa, the walls of which can still be found. After 62 years, in 1742, a few families returned to the Rio Grande Valley to found the modern pueblo. The old mission remains visible, although reduced to a rubble of adobe. Sandia Pueblo remains a small village, containing less than 150 people.

SAN FELIPE PUEBLO

San Felipe is one of the most conservative of the pueblos and has retained much of its Indian heritage despite the impact of Spanish and American influences. It has a close affinity with its neighbors, particularly Santo Domingo only five miles distant. San Felipe was a well-established village when the Spanish first arrived. Its people joined in heartily when the pueblo uprising began in 1680 but abandoned their village during a Spanish counteroffensive in 1681 (which failed). When reconquest was completed in 1692, the people returned to their village. Thereafter, they remained friendly to the Spanish and suffered many attacks from the Navajo, who hated them for this loyalty.

One of the finest remaining structures showing early Franciscan mission architecture can be seen at the San Felipe church. The present church is not the original mission, for three different churches were located at San Felipe over the centuries. The first was built in 1605 and destroyed during the Pueblo Revolt. The second was built in a new part of the village in 1694, but shortly after 1700, the village was moved and a new church constructed. The latter church is the one now in use at San Felipe. On May 1, the nearly 1000 people of the pueblo celebrate their annual fiesta.

San Ildefonso Pueblo

San Ildefonso has gained fame throughout the world because of the excellence of its pottery. The high quality and general acceptance of this commodity has made the village prosperous. It boasts some of the most famous Indian artists and artisans in the United States, among them Julian and Maria Martinez, perhaps the best-known potters in the world.

San Ildefonso participated in the Pueblo Revolt but did not contest the reconquest, at least not at first. In 1694, when de Vargas began to wage war on the northern pueblos, San Ildefonso did take part. The people fortified themselves on Black Mesa, a high, steep mesa of volcanic origin near the pueblo. There they successfully withstood Spanish efforts to dislodge them. Notwithstanding their initial success, they were ultimately conquered and brought into the Spanish system. Today there are several hundred people living in the village, and they are among the friendliest of the pueblo peoples. San Ildefonso is easily accessible from Santa Fe.

The mission church dates back to the 1890's, although earlier churches at the pueblo played an important role in bringing Christianity to the Pueblo Indian world. The older churches are long since gone.

San Juan Pueblo

San Juan Pueblo is best noted for its close association with the first Spanish settlement in New Mexico in 1598. Oñate, colonizer of New Mexico, selected a site for his first headquarters which was a part of the ancient Pueblo of San Juan. The natives living in that part of the village willingly gave up their homes to the Spaniards and were taken in by the remainder of the people of San Juan. Oñate, in appreciation for this hospitality, bestowed upon the pueblo the name *San Juan de los Caballeros,* a name which the pueblo is still proud to bear.

Yet this same friendly people also contributed Po-pé, the great leader of the Pueblo Revolt, to the history of New Mexico. While Po-pé shared with many other pueblo leaders a hatred of the Spanish conqueror, he was the spiritual force and the organizer of the rebellion that broke the control of the Spaniard for twelve years and returned New Mexico to the Indian. This great rebellion stands as one of the significant efforts in the history of the world of a people to cast off the bonds of foreign control.

San Juan cannot claim a church dating back to the *conquistadores,* but it does have one of the great landmark churches in the Southwest. In 1890, the chapel of Our Lady of Lourdes was dedicated at San Juan. It was constructed of red volcanic rock found west of the Rio Grande. This beautiful structure is an architectural jewel set in desert surroundings.

The nearly 700 people of San Juan welcome visitors to their homes; their undecorated burnished black pottery is particularly distinctive and popular. The pueblo's annual festival is held in June.

SANTA ANA PUEBLO

Santa Ana Pueblo lies along the banks of the Rio Jemez, which enters the Rio Grande from the west. The pueblo was visited by Oñate and a mission was built there about 1600, shortly after his visit. The people of Santa Ana joined in the Pueblo Revolt, and since there was no priest serving their church in 1680, they joined with the Indians of Santo Domingo and San Felipe to massacre the padres at San Felipe. In 1687, during one of the Spanish efforts to reconquer New Mexico, Santa Ana was destroyed and her people fled. Later, at the urging of de Vargas, the modern pueblo was established, along with the church now standing there. The population of Santa Ana is nearly 400. Its annual festival takes place in August. It is often difficult to find many of the people at the main pueblo for they spend most of the growing season at El Ranchito, to the east in the Rio Grande Valley.

SANTA CLARA PUEBLO

Santa Clara Pueblo is near the mouth of Santa Clara Creek, a year-round stream flowing out of the Jemez Mountains into the Rio Grande. To the west of the pueblo, on lands owned by Santa Clara, are the famous Puye Cliff Dwellings ruins. The people of Santa Clara claim these natural cliff homes as their ancestral dwelling places, a fact which has been substantiated by archeologists. The Santa Clara Indians represent, then, an important living Indian group in which one can observe institutions and traditions that can be linked to traditions of the cultures that lived in the caves and abandoned cities of Southwest antiquity.

Like most of the pueblo people, Santa Clara joined the Pueblo Revolt, but this action did not seriously harm the pueblo. The real damage was done to Santa Clara in the late eighteenth century when intertribal warfare over witchcraft, plus the ravages of disease, took nearly 500 lives in the village. The current population is about 500.

The church at Santa Clara is quite modern, having been constructed in the twentieth century. The old church, built in 1760, was caught up in the modernization craze that swept through the pueblo world in the early 1900's. Perhaps one of the most substantial and beautiful of all pueblo churches, the old church collapsed during a storm in 1909 (the same storm that destroyed the church at Nambé); it had been structurally weakened by the removal of the roof for remodeling.

The village has excellent agricultural lands and supplements its income by manufacturing an excellent and distinctive pure black pottery. Its annual festival is in mid-August.

SANTO DOMINGO PUEBLO

Santo Domingo is one of the largest of the pueblos, having a population of nearly 1500. It is also the most conservative in retention of its native culture. This makes its dances and dress of particular interest to the visitor to New Mexico. The present pueblo was established after the reconquest in 1692. The Indians of Santo Domingo took a particularly active part in the Pueblo Revolt, killing three padres resident at the pueblo. When de Vargas moved to retake Santo Domingo, he found the people had abandoned the village. They had constructed a village in the Jemez Mountains to the west, and it was there that de Vargas defeated them. Even then, the people of Santo Domingo did not give up the fight, and only after a long series of defeats and serious loss of life did they surrender and again return to the vicinity of their original village.

The church at Santo Domingo is not so old as many other pueblo edifices, but its qualities remain among the most typical aspects of early New Mexico mission architecture. In early August, during the great annual festival, the Indians completely clean and whitewash the church. Two large horses are painted on the front of the building by native artists. The dances during the Santo Domingo festival are among the most colorful and authentic in New Mexico.

Taos Pueblo

Taos represents the northernmost of the pueblos in New Mexico. It is also one of the most scenic, lying at the foot of the Taos Mountains, a spur of the mighty Sangre de Cristo range. It is a prosperous village of about 900 persons. There is no finer example of pueblo apartment architecture in New Mexico. The main pueblo building rises five stories above the mesa. One must be careful not to confuse the Spanish town, don Fernando de Taos, and the old Indian farming center, Ranchos de Taos, with the pueblo, San Geronimo de Taos. It is the latter that is Indian and is, therefore, by far the oldest of the three.

The ruins of the old San Geronimo mission at Taos represent one of the most historic and fateful in all the Southwest. It was there that two priests were murdered in 1680 during the first days of the Pueblo Revolt. It was there that Po-pé sowed the first seeds of that rebellion. Again in 1696, the Taos Indians sought to free themselves from Spanish control by killing their priests and other Spaniards in the vicinity. Again they were subdued. In 1847, when the Americans annexed New Mexico, the Taos Indians tried once more to gain their independence. Inflamed by Mexican citizens who refused to accept American authority, they attacked the Americans at Fernando de Taos, killing nine of them. Governor Charles Bent, builder of the famous Bent's Fort on the Santa Fe Trail, was among those killed. On February 3, 1847, the American army in New Mexico laid siege to the village and the Indians fortified themselves in the mission. It became the Alamo of the Taos people. American artillery was brought to bear, and the walls of the ancient church were battered down; the Indians fled, first to the village and then into the mountains, leaving behind 150 dead and many wounded. They were finally forced to surrender, and their leaders were hung. Those so hung remain martyrs to this day. The ruins of the Taos mission, built three and a quar-

SOUVENIR OF THE AMERICAN ARMY'S WORK IN 1847: TAOS PUEBLO MISSION

ter centuries ago, still can be seen. They are a stark landmark to the stubborn independence of the people of Taos.

The traditions and ceremonials of Taos are well preserved. Their arts and crafts, however, have declined and are not of the high quality found in some of the other pueblos. Their ceremonials are excellent and are noted for their beauty and precision. The feast day of San Geronimo, September 30, is the most important event of the year.

TESUQUE PUEBLO

Tesuque is a small village, perhaps numbering no more than 150 persons. Even though it has always been small, it holds a major place in the history of New Mexico. It was at Tesuque that the first blood was shed in the Pueblo Revolt of 1680. On August 9, Cristobal de Herrera was murdered, and two Tesuque Indians rushed to Santa Fe to warn the Spanish governor of the impending rebellion. The Indian leaders, now aware that their plot was known, moved the date of the revolt from August 13 to

MOST-PAINTED CHURCH IN AMERICA? . . . RANCHOS DE TAOS

August 10. On August 10, Father Pio, in charge of the Tesuque mission, went out from Santa Fe to say Mass and also was murdered.

Although its handicrafts are of poor quality, the Tesuque Indian ceremonials are colorful and authentic. The people have retained much of their early culture while living in proximity to the white man (Santa Fe is only nine miles distant). The pueblo's most important festival falls on November 12.

ZIA PUEBLO

The story of Zia is one of tragedy and difficult problems of existence. Located on a basalt flow on the north bank of the Jemez River some fifteen miles above its junction with the Rio Grande, Zia has poor land and a limited supply of irrigation water. Agriculture is the main economic pursuit, but the pueblo's unfortunate location makes trading for part of its food supply necessary.

Oñate reported Zia to be a large pueblo. However, it suffered greatly because of its participation in the Pueblo Revolt. Some historians estimate that during the reconquest, nearly 600 of the people of Zia were killed defending themselves from the Spanish. Continued wars and pestilence reduced the pueblo to a very few families. Over the past century, the group has again showed signs of growth and now has a population of more than 300.

The church at Zia dates from 1692, and thus represents one of the fine examples of ancient Franciscan architecture in New Mexico. The annual festival, dedicated to Nuestra Senora de la Asuncion, is celebrated with an excellent Corn Dance on August 15.

Zuni Pueblo

Zuni has the distinction of being the first of the pueblos seen or visited by Europeans. Seen from a distance by Fray Marcos de Niza in 1539, it was reported as a rich and extensive city. Nearby were six other pueblos, and the Spanish immediately associated the Zuni complex with an old Spanish legend about seven golden cities, the Seven Cities of Cibola. The expedition of Coronado was formed to explore and conquer the rich pueblos of New Mexico. His first contact was at Zuni, then called *Hawikuh*. It was neither golden nor rich.

Although Zuni was an important stopping place on the early trails to Mexico, it managed to remain least influenced by European ideas. The Spanish concentrated their efforts in the Rio Grande Valley and Zuni went its own way most of the time. While there were missionary efforts from time to time, by the nineteenth century, the stout resistance to such activity caused it to cease. In recent years, sporadic missionary activity has been evident, but it has not been notably successful.

The most famous of all New Mexico Indian ceremonial dances is held at Zuni each year. The Shalako, which occurs in early December, is authentic and spectacular. The dancers, carrying huge ceremonial figures on their shoulders, must train and practice constantly during the entire year.

Zuni is the largest of the pueblos in New Mexico, with a population numbering more than 5000 persons. The main occupation is agriculture. The Zunis supplement their income by manufacturing silver inlay jewelry that shows great creative skill and is beautiful to behold.

Other New Mexico Indians

In addition to the well-known Pueblo Indians of New Mexico, there are four other areas of Indian lands. Three of these belong to peoples of Athapascan origin, sometimes better known as Apache Indians. By name, they are the Jicarilla Apache, the Mescalero Apache, and Navajo. The fourth group is the Ute Indian.

The Apache tribes were relative newcomers to the Southwest. Their origin was the plains area between the northern Rocky Mountains and Hudson Bay in Canada. About 1000 A.D., a part of these northern Plains Indians began a migration that ultimately brought them to New Mexico. Down the High Plains across the western Dakotas, western Nebraska, Kansas, and finally to western Texas and eastern New Mexico, these people came. At about the latitude of Albuquerque, the migration split. Part of the group continued south, across the Staked Plains, into south-eastern New Mexico, west Texas, and northern Coahuila and Chihuahua, Mexico. Here they divided into the Lipan, the Mescalero, and the Natage

Apache. Today, in south-central New Mexico are the descendants of the Mescalero. The Mescalero Apache reservation is crossed by U.S. Highway 70, a scenic drive through pine forests. The tribe operates the Sierra Blanca ski area, one of the southernmost ski areas in the United States. Its annual Crown Dance and coming-of-age ceremonials are held July 1 to 4, followed by an Apache rodeo. The Lipan and the Natage have virtually disappeared.

The second group of the migration discovered for the first time in their long trek down the eastern fringes of the Rockies that the country opened up to the west. They poured through the passes and entered the areas traditionally controlled by pueblo farmers. Gradually, they took over these lands for themselves, driving out the farmers. By the time the Spanish came on the scene, most of the peaceful farmers had given way before the onslaught of the warlike Athapascan savages. Only one group remained, the pueblos of the central Rio Grande Valley. The migration that moved into the desert and mountain lands divided into a number of groups which are known by modern names: the Chiricahua, White Mountain, Western, and Jicarilla Apache and the Navajo. The Jicarilla Apache reside mainly in north-central New Mexico on reservation lands, and the Navajo reservation lies partly in extreme northwestern New Mexico. Most of the Navajo land and all the lands of the others are in Arizona.

The Ute Indians, driven from the plains by stronger tribes, settled in the central Rocky Mountain area. There they raided the wealthy (at least in their eyes) pueblos to the south. They fought sporadically against white penetration but were finally subdued and placed on reservation lands in the Four Corners area, part of which lies in New Mexico.

While the history of these peoples is fascinating and full of romance, there is little besides scenery to be seen when visiting their reservations. The populations are often scattered over many hundreds of square miles, and the people have only rudimentary handicrafts. The exception is the Navajo, and a trip to the Navajo reservation is worthwhile. These Indians have developed techniques of weaving and silversmithing that contribute significant art forms to Southwest handicrafts.

The outstanding Indian event of the year in New Mexico is the Inter-Tribal Indian Ceremonial at Gallup, held during mid-August. Some thirty tribes from the Southwest and Midwest meet to compete in arts, crafts, and ceremonial dancing.

Reminders of the Past

by PAIGE W. CHRISTIANSEN

When driving across New Mexico or when visiting some part of the state, one should be aware of the wealth of history that is always close at hand. Many people, when faced with what seems like endless miles of empty country, fail to realize that the very emptiness is one of the charms of the state. They also do not recognize that in the vast expanses of mountain and desert, people of the ancient past or a recent past have lived and worked and died. Sometimes the fruits of their labor are clear and evident and live on in cities and towns. In many instances, however, the mountains and desert have reclaimed their own and the works of man have succumbed. A mental picture must be cast over the landscape on which great historical events took place but which is almost empty of signs of man's efforts. If travelers are fortunate, there may still be some sign—a ghost town, a ruined ranch, some old artifacts—to tell the story; if not, imagination must be given rein. The search is the adventure, and to give aid in that search, the following might suffice as a faint guiding light.

To simplify the descriptions of these reminders of the past, New Mexico is divided into seven geographical regions which a traveler might well visit:

1. *North from Santa Fe,* including U.S. Highways 64, 285, and 84, and connecting state highways.

2. *The northeast,* including U.S. 85 from Santa Fe to Raton, U.S. 66 east from Albuquerque to the Texas line, U.S. 56 from Springer to the state line, and connecting state highways.

3. *The northwest,* including U.S. 66 west from Albuquerque to the Arizona line, U.S. 666 north from Gallup to Colorado, and State Highway 44 from Bernalillo to Farmington.

4. *East-central,* including U.S. 60 east from Bernardo, U.S. 380 east from San Antonio, U.S. 70 from the Mescalero Indian Reservation to the Texas line, U.S. 285 from Clines Corners to Roswell, U.S. 54 from Three Rivers to Santa Rosa, and connecting state highways.

5. *West-central,* including U.S. 60 west of Socorro, U.S. 180-260 and State Highway 12 in Catron County, U.S. 85 from Los Lunas to Elephant Butte, and connecting state highways.

6. *Southeast,* including U.S. 70 from Las Cruces to the Mescalero Indian Reservation, U.S. 54 from El Paso to Three Rivers, U.S. 62 from Hobbs to the Texas line, U.S. 285 from Roswell to the Texas line, and numerous state roads.

7. *Southwest,* including U.S. 85 from Truth or Consequences to El Paso, U.S. 180 north from Deming to the Catron county line, U.S. 70-80 west from Las Cruces to Arizona, and state roads.

NORTH FROM SANTA FE

The country north of Santa Fe is the heart of Indian and Spanish New Mexico. Here, if he looks beyond the narrow boundaries of the highway right-of-way, the traveler can see Indian and Spanish villages which have not changed significantly in two and a half centuries. Along the lush green of the Rio Grande Valley or of its tributaries dashing out of the Sangre de Cristo range to the east, these sleepy concentrations of people reveal cultural and language patterns which smack of the *conquistadores* of the sixteenth century or of the ancient cliff dwellers. It is a slow and easy world, perhaps most representative of the "land of mañana." In a region already worked for centuries for what it can produce, there is no hurry. It will be there tomorrow and forever. The people of this region are typically New Mexican. The hills are dotted with piñon and juniper trees which give a greenish to black cast to the land. This, too, is typically New Mexican.

(Forest Service, U.S.D.A.)

COOL DRIVE ON A SUMMER DAY, RED RIVER CANYON

There is one short trip that would be fruitful for him who wants to know New Mexico, to feel the romance of Spanish culture, and to seek adventure off the beaten track. Just north of Espanola, State Highway 76 strikes east from U.S. 64. Nowhere in the state can be found so much of old world charm or spectacular scenic beauty. Heading east, the traveler passes through Chimayó, a village famed throughout the world for its weaving, though seldom visited, then on through Truchas and Las Trampas to Penasco, heart of the Penitente country. The Penitentes were a religious sect growing out of long isolation from the main threads of Roman Catholicism. They gradually reverted to relatively primitive Christian practices without guidance from main church centers but within the past few years have returned to the Church. The many white crosses that can be seen in the area attest to their former activity. From Penasco, the traveler can return to U.S. 64 via State Highway 75.

The area northwest of Santa Fe, stretching some thirty or forty miles on the southeast flanks of the Jemez Mountains, is the noted Pajarito Plateau, the home of great numbers of Indian cultures, living and dead. Many of the modern Indian pueblos will be found in this region. Also, some of the most significant ancient Indian ruins are found here, such as the Frijoles Canyon (Bandelier National Monument) and Puye Cliff Dwellings.

The entire area north of Santa Fe, then, is alive with history. In every village, in every canyon, there is something that will add to the romance of Spanish–Indian New Mexico. In our Southwest, the heritage handed down by these two great cultures is held dear by the people. To the traveler will come a greater appreciation and a greater understanding of New Mexico and the Southwest if these are but understood.

Northeast New Mexico

The section designated as northeast New Mexico is an area of mountains and plains, and its historical mosaic shows elements of both: the rugged Sandia Mountains near Albuquerque and the southernmost parts of the extensive Sangre de Cristo range, which thrusts north from U.S. Highway 85 far into Colorado, and part of the famed buffalo plains. The area is drained by two main river systems; the Canadian River flows east to join the Arkansas and the Mississippi and the Pecos River flows south to join the Rio Grande.

Through this vast area ran one of America's greatest highways, the Santa Fe Trail. Beginning in Missouri communities, the Trail hurled itself into the intricate patterns of the Great Plains with all of their dangers—Indians, boredom, violent storms, treacherous rivers, and prairie grass fires. Then on into the foothills of the mighty Rocky Mountains and the steep and backbreaking approaches to Raton Pass in New Mexico. The new highway across this pass (U.S. 85) and the nature of our vehicles have made this an easy passage. But the traveler should pause at some high point, or perhaps leave the main highway for a moment, and try to imagine crossing this rugged land in Conestoga wagons. From Raton, the Santa Fe

How to see the Rio Grande Valley—from Sandia Crest

Trail continued south to Las Vegas and thence into Santa Fe via Glorieta Pass (current route of U.S. 85). Over this trail passed the goods of the world. In part, these were intended for the people of New Mexico, but over other trails they also found markets in Mexico and in California. For the curious and adventurous, sections of the Santa Fe Trail can still be seen. Local inquiry will elicit directions to remaining parts of the wide rutted Trail, scene of so much of the American westward movement.

While passing through the mountains between Santa Fe and Las Vegas, the traveler should be aware that a critical Civil War battle was waged in the fastness of these passes. In 1862, Confederate forces, which came up the Rio Grande from Texas and won a series of victories over Union troops, met a combined force of Colorado Volunteers and New Mexico Union troops in a decisive contest over the control of the American Southwest. The Union troops were successful, preserving New Mexico and the West for the Union.

These, then, are some of the things to look for in this region of plains and mountains. Picture buffalo by the tens of thousands pushing up the Canadian River, or long lines of wagons winding their way along the Santa Fe Trail carrying goods and people into new lands, or the Blue and the Gray locked in deadly combat far from the thunder of the main Civil War battles. The mosaic here is sharp and vividly different.

137

Northwest New Mexico is typified as ancient Indian country. While seemingly a harsh land, it is only this to the uninitiated, to those who lock their minds to beauties of history and lands unlike their own. The Indian found this country good and productive. Some of the finest ruins of Indian antiquity are in this region—Chaco Canyon and Aztec, both National Monuments, and hundreds more that remain unnamed. The Indians of the Four Corners area (named thus because New Mexico, Colorado, Utah, and Arizona meet here, the only place in the United States where the lines of four states intersect) created levels of culture unsurpassed in what is the continental United States; only the Indians of Mexico and Peru claim a higher culture. This is a land whose ancient people reached their great peak at the same time as the later Romans, as Charlemagne in ancient Frankish Europe, and as Mohammed and his successors in the Middle East.

But ancient Indians hold no monopoly on this vast region. Today many of the Indians of New Mexico still find homes here. The Navajo Reservation lies between Gallup and the Colorado line. Part of the Ute Reservation lies along the northern edge of New Mexico, and the Jicarilla Reservation is in the eastern part of this region. Many of the pueblo people are found between Albuquerque and Santa Fe. At Gallup each year, the famed Indian Ceremonials bring together peoples from many of the tribes in the United States.

This region is also renowned as an oil and natural gas producer and is one of the booming areas in New Mexico. But this is only one aspect of the mineral riches of the northwest; the mines near Grants, between Albuquerque and Gallup, produce tremendous quantities of uranium ores. The atomic energy capability of the United States begins at Grants. And near Gallup and Fruitland are huge open-pit coal mines.

The northwest is drained by the San Juan River, a tributary of the Colorado River, and is therefore a part of the Pacific watershed. The Navajo Dam project, just east of Farmington, is a part of this drainage pattern.

Thus the region is characterized by Indians old and new, ancient things buried deep beneath the earth, and great beauty in pastel colors and subtle contrasts—the mosaic of the land.

East-Central New Mexico

East-central New Mexico, like the northeast, is an area of plains and mountains. Here the buffalo roamed, and in their place, cattle now utilize the hardy and nutritious grasses of the High Plains. Mountains are the Manzano, southeast of Albuquerque, and Sierra Blanca, near Carrizozo, as well as numerous minor ranges. Also in this region is some harsh and desolate country, seared by the southwestern sun and lacking in rainfall, but supporting the exotic plants and wildlife typical of the Sonoran desert regions.

While the desert regions may not be attractive to the eye, they should be appreciated for their part in the historical mosaic. In the area east of the Rio Grande is the northern half of the well-known White Sands Missile Range, one of the significant test centers in the rocket and space age. It was also in this arid region that the first atomic bomb was exploded (southeast of Socorro).

The early use of this desert, however, emphasized its harshness. For centuries, the Spanish suffered across this waterless waste on their way from Chihuahua in Old Mexico to Santa Fe, for this was the Jornada del Muerto, journey of death, the hardest and most dangerous part of the trip over the Camino Real. The Camino Real was the lifeline of New Mexico from 1598 until the Santa Fe Trail was opened in 1821, and all visitors during that period were obliged to cross this arid section. A modern rocket crosses in mere seconds what took the Spaniards many days.

In the Manzano Mountains, there are numerous Indian ruins which represent the eastern fringes of the pueblo-building Indians of New Mexico. These ruined villages have been given the name by historians of "cities that died of fear," fear of the vicious Apache and Comanche tribes. For centuries, these brave village people tilled their crops and lived peacefully on the land. Then, in the thirteenth, fourteenth, and fifteenth cen-

(Forest Service, U.S.D.A.)

Who says this is desert country? . . . Sierra Blanca from U.S. 70

139

turies, the great migrations of Plains Indians that pushed into the Southwest gradually did their deadly work. One by one the villages succumbed,
until by 1700 few people remained, and these were ultimately killed or
driven into the sanctuary of the Rio Grande pueblos. It is awesome to stand
'mid the rubble of one of those ancient cities and imagine the circumstances of its demise.

In the eastern part of this section was the heart of the High Plains
cattle empires. Here is a land that once belonged to the great cattle barons,
a land of free range, the home of the cowboy. Although it is fenced today,
it is still a land of cattle and is still very close to the early days of the
cattleman.

Again, there is an intricate and varied mosaic. No simple land this, but
a complexity of plains, mountains, and desert, all of which color its
history. The Indians no longer inhabit their villages, the Spanish no longer
struggle along the Jornada del Muerto, and the free range of the cattle
baron is gone, but if the traveler sees it through its historical past, it will
again come alive.

WEST-CENTRAL NEW MEXICO

This section is a complex and colorful mass of landforms scattered
helter-skelter across the western part of the state. It stretches from the
green Rio Grande Valley, with its irrigated lands, quaint farms, and
picturesque agricultural villages, up the Valley's steep western slopes to the
rolling grassland and mesas and alluvial fans, ending in precipitous and
treacherous canyons in the rugged mountains. Socorro Mountain, the
Magdalenas, the San Mateos, the Ladrones, and countless others seem always to ring the horizon. Some of them are timbered and abound in cool,
refreshing shade and springs; some are harsh and dry. In the west, the
famed San Agustin Plains stretch to the sunset, a wide carpet fringed by
black, timbered hills, site of fabulous cattle drives of a bygone day. The
complexity of the region's geology, scenery, and terrain is matched by an
equally complex history.

The history is a mosaic of many hues, some harsh and stark like its
dry desert mountains, some inviting like the shade and coolness of its
timbered canyons and mountain springs. First were the many diverse and
sometimes hostile Indian cultures. There were peaceful pueblo peoples
tilling their lands, using the Rio Grande's flowing water to produce
abundance. Also, prehistoric village dwellers struggled to create agricultural societies along the banks of now-dry rivers in the western part of
the region. And there were the fearsome Apache Indians who founded
their homes in the broken mountain fastnesses and added their excitement
and tragedy to the mosaic. So, too, did the Spaniard make his mark and
the Mexican who followed close behind. The place names of the eastern
part of the region are primarily Spanish, although the Spanish found the
area a difficult one in which to maintain themselves. And then the American came to dominate this land, adding realism and technology.

140

Finally, two major economic factors left a profound imprint: stock raising and mining. The first began with the Spanish, was continued by the Mexicans, and commercialized by the Americans. Everywhere are signs of this heritage. Mining also played a dominant role, although of a shorter duration. One can hardly lift his eyes to the hills without seeing signs of the prospector's shovel or the miner's work. One can hardly converse with local citizens without discussing mines of the past or mines of the future. Livestock and minerals, then, are woven through the historical pattern and are never far from any part of the story.

Let the traveler be aware of several important facts when he passes through this region. First, this is empty country, an area that has fewer people now than it had eighty years ago. Its mines are mostly closed and the towns that grew with the mines are ghosts. One of the most famous of these is the town of Kelly, a short distance from the community of Magdalena. Another is Mogollon, off U.S. Highway 180 in the south-western part of this region. Either of these will give to the viewer a vivid picture of the mining camps of the nineteenth century.

To the average tourist crossing the San Agustin Plains, they seem desolate and uninteresting. To the traveler with imagination and knowledge of the history of this once great inland lake, the trip can be exciting. He pictures this great basin full of water, forty-five miles long and fifteen miles wide, and sees mountains covered with blue spruce surrounding the great lake. His mental motion picture rolls on thousands of years, watching the water evaporate and the forest of spruce die, to be replaced eventually by the piñon and juniper now dotting the hills. Grass grew in the old lake bed, except in the last areas to evaporate, for these had an alkali content too high for most grasses. The traveler then watches the Indian enter the scene—not the pueblo builder, except as a transient, for no water is available. The nomadic warrior uses the pathway later. In 1774 and in 1776, he sees several important battles between the Spanish and the Apaches fought on these Plains. Later, the American cattleman dominates them, as he does today. . . .

And so the mosaic grows—Indians, Spanish, Americans, cattle, and mines—and the spectacular vistas and the vast emptiness add color and excitement for the traveler who sees the past with the present.

Southeast New Mexico

Much of southeast New Mexico is an extension of the Great Plains, but it has some rugged mountains and a severe desert in the middle of which lie White Sands National Monument and the White Sands Missile Range. Mountain ranges include the Sacramento east of Alamogordo and the Guadalupe Mountains, in which are located Carlsbad Caverns.

The plains part of this region are devoted to cattle, potash, and oil. Like the other plains regions of New Mexico, the heritage passed on from the great cattle empires of bygone days is very strong and detectable in the people. Since the early 1930's, oil has come to play an increasingly im-

141

ANYONE FOR A HIKE? . . . IN THE GUADALUPE MOUNTAINS

portant part in the history of this section. This is especially true near Hobbs.

The desert region in the western part of this section has clearly defined aspects of the old and the new. The southern part of the dread Jornado del Muerto swept across this arid land and only returned to the river near modern Hatch, or sometimes farther south, near modern Las Cruces, according to the whim of the river. Here also lies the White Sands National

Monument, a desert spot of unusual beauty and interest. Near the Monument, the White Sands Missile Range stands as an advanced scientific test center for the most modern of vehicles, the rocket. Near Alamogordo, another advanced space development and testing facility is located at Holloman Air Force Base. So the desert is useful, and it is beautiful, and it is full of tragic history.

This is also Indian land. East of Tularosa is the Mescalero Apache Indian Reservation. In a way, this region has always belonged to the Apache, at least since he migrated into New Mexico. The area contained no sedentary groups and the Apache appropriated it as his own. His strongholds were in the Guadalupe and Sacramento mountains. The forts along the Rio Grande, like Forts Fillmore and Selden, were located to control the Mescalero and other Apache groups. All that remains today are the Mescaleros.

There was little Spanish influence in this area except near El Paso and in the Rio Grande Valley. The Spanish were more attracted to the upper Rio Grande Valley because of the sedentary nature of the Indians of that region. The southeast underwent its greatest development in the American period.

Again, sense the mosaic: These are not blends of land and history; they are sharp and distinct, each with its own character. Search for the history and the beauty, for they do not come automatically.

SOUTHWEST NEW MEXICO

Finally, the southwest, another region of harsh desert and cool refreshing mountains, part of New Mexico's unusual contrast. The country south of U.S. 70 is Sonoran desert, thinly populated and poorly watered. To the north of the highway lies one of the most spectacular beauty spots in the Southwest, the mountains and forests forming the headwaters of the Gila River. The Gila River flows west across Arizona until it joins the Colorado River which empties into the Gulf of California.

The Indians in this part of the state fall into two distinct categories: The builders, known as the Mimbres culture, constructed homes in caves and along the watercourses of the Gila and Mimbres rivers. They reached extremely high levels of culture, and then they disappeared. The Apache Indians, who entered this country at the same time as they did the rest of New Mexico, were responsible for the end of the farmers and builders, at least in part. The Apaches were predators and the farmers were peaceful, unversed in the arts of war. Finally the Apache ruled supreme, and this region became the most important single stronghold of the Indian. It was here that Geronimo found sanctuary. But the Apaches, too, were forced to surrender their claims and were placed on reservations outside this area.

Mining is and has been the main source of wealth. The great open-pit operation of Kennecott Copper Company is at Santa Rita, east of Silver City. This is one of the largest open-pit copper mines in North America. To look into that huge man-made pit is a thrilling experience. This mine was first opened in 1803 by the Spanish who needed copper badly as a circulating currency in New Spain (Mexico). For a number of years, the coins used for money in Mexico were from copper mined in southwestern New Mexico.

Copper represents only a part of the mining activity in this region. Famous mining districts in earlier days were at Kingston and Hillsboro, just east of the Black Range on State Highway 90. These areas produced considerable quantities of silver. There is some activity yet, but the boom has long since passed them by, although they are interesting towns to visit. The trip from U.S. 85 to Silver City via State Highway 90 is one of the most scenic routes in the state.

In the region north of Silver City lies high mountain country, much of it preserved as the Gila Wilderness Area. Here a person who wishes the solitude of forest and mountain, the thrill of trout fishing in a clear cold stream, and a wealth of wildlife can find his heart's desire. In the heart of this wilderness, the traveler might well find some of the ancient homes of the Mimbres people. History and recreation blend into one.

These complete the mosaic. Everywhere one travels in New Mexico is enchanting history, in the land and/or in the people. This has not been an effort to acquaint anyone with the intricate detail of all the history of every nook and cranny of this land, but these broad strokes made on the canvas may help the traveler, transient or native, to enjoy himself. Let him accept the challenge, stop to investigate, search out evidence of the history that is there in the colorful and changing land itself, the Indian heritage, the Spanish past, the cattleman's range, the miner's endless search—and become enchanted.

(Forest Service, U.S.D.A., by John Whiteside)

WHEELER PEAK NEAR TAOS—HIGHEST POINT IN NEW MEXICO, 13,160 FEET ABOVE SEA LEVEL

(Courtesy Elliott S. Barker)

GHOST RANCH MOUNTAIN NORTH OF ABIQUIU

Derricks and Mines

by George B. Griswold

New Mexico is a mineral-rich state. The gross production value of oil, gas, and minerals was $671 million during 1963, making the state the sixth ranking mineral producer in the nation. New Mexico ranks among other states as follows: first in the production of potash, uranium, perlite, and carbon dioxide; third in helium; fourth in copper; fifth in natural gas and liquids; and seventh in petroleum. Important amounts of zinc, lead, gold, silver, magnesium compounds, coal, gypsum, pumice, and salt are also produced from deposits within New Mexico. The oil and gas industry holds a dominant position in the state, accounting for almost two thirds of the value of minerals produced.

OIL AND GAS

Most of New Mexico's oil and gas are produced in the southeastern part, south and east of Roswell. The bustling towns of Hobbs, Artesia, and Lovington, as well as Roswell, are headquarters for the many oil companies and the associated service and supply organizations operating in the area. Oil and gas are produced from numerous reservoirs, called *fields* or *pools,* in Paleozoic sediments ranging from Ordovician to Permian in age. From the standpoint of production, the Eunice–Monument field (lying between these two towns) is the largest, having produced more than 250 million barrels of oil. Other important fields are Hobbs, Vacuum, Langlie Mattix, Denton, and Jalmat. All these fields produce a considerable amount of gas associated directly with the oil.

When driving an automobile through southeast New Mexico, a layman finds it difficult to comprehend the immensity of the petroleum industry of that region. This is due to the scattering of wells over a large area. Seldom are wells spaced closer than one to every ten acres, even in the most productive fields. There are, in fact, some 16,000 wells in this part of New Mexico, ranging in depth from less than 1000 feet to 17,555 feet.

The other oil- and gas-producing area of the state is in the northwest, in the San Juan Basin. Farmington serves as the base of operations for most of this activity. In 1962, there were 7378 wells in the area, 1770 of which were producing oil and gas and 5608 producing gas only. Most of the San Juan Basin production is from Cretaceous sandstones, in contrast to the southeast where the oil and gas are derived from Paleozoic sediments. The development of the San Juan Basin production is relatively new; most of the wells have been drilled since World War II. The petroleum industry can be proud of the great help it has given to the development of this once-almost-forgotten part of the state.

(*Courtesy El Paso Natural Gas Co.*)

THERE'S THE WAY TO REFINE OIL! LOOK AT THOSE MESAS, NEAR GALLUP

The methods of finding and producing oil and gas have come a long way from the "boom town" days when wells were drilled for the most part on pure hunches and hopes. The exploration and exploitation of petroleum are now highly specialized technologies. All branches of the geologic and geophysical sciences are brought into play to piece together a comprehensive picture of all the factors which may have made a certain area favorable for the accumulation of oil or gas. These factors include such things as the age, thickness, and permeability of the sedimentary rocks, the structure, old shorelines, and buried reefs. Once a target is selected, a drilling rig is moved onto the location to prove or disprove the theory. This is the costly step of finding oil. A single 10,000-foot hole may cost $350,000, and some individual wells in New Mexico have cost more than $1 million to drill. If the well is in a completely untested area, it is called a "wildcat." Once a discovery is made, then the land around the wildcat is explored by "offset" wells until the complete extent of the new field is proved.

During 1962, 1666 wells were drilled to an average depth of 5153 feet. The average drilling cost was $71,000 a well, representing a total investment of almost $120 million in a single year! Most of these wells were of the development (offset) type, but even then, 27 per cent were dry. During 1962, 295 true wildcats were drilled; of these, only 46 found oil or gas—about two out of every thirteen.

The story of oil just begins with the discovery of a well. Various special "completion" operations are applied to the oil-producing horizon so as to increase the flow into the well. The most common techniques are either by

147

"acidizing," pumping acid into the formation to increase flow by enlarging the pores in the rock, or by "hydrafracing," whereby actual cracks are induced in the formation by pumping oil from the surface back into the well under very high pressure. After the well is "completed," it may be a natural-flowing well if sufficient gas is associated with the oil. If sufficient gas is not present, then the well is pumped.

In recent years, considerable success has been achieved in revitalizing old fields where production had dropped below the point of economic operation. These fields are reactivated by forcing either water or gas down selected wells within the field, thereby forcing stagnated oil within the producing zone toward the other wells. This technique is called *secondary recovery*. Many fields will produce more oil under the secondary recovery

HERE'S A WILDCAT FOR YOU!

program than they did during their primary life.

Once the oil is on the surface, it passes through separators to remove any admixed gas from the oil. The gas is sent into pipelines while the oil is sent to storage tanks called *tank batteries*. Periodically, the oil is drawn from the tank batteries where it is transported by pipeline or rail to refineries. The great bulk of the crude oil leaves New Mexico for refining via a major pipeline network extending through Texas to both the Gulf and East coasts. Some oil is refined in New Mexico, however. Oil refineries in Artesia, Bloomfield, Ciniza, Farmington, and Monument have a combined capacity to treat some 30,000 barrels (42 gallons a barrel) of crude oil a day. On the other hand, practically all the natural gas is treated in New Mexico so as to recover its liquid petroleum constituents before sending it out of the state by pipeline.

MINING

The mining industry of New Mexico dates back to the days of Spanish rule. Copper was mined from the Santa Rita mine as early as 1800 for shipment to Mexico for use in coinage. Significant mining in New Mexico did not commence, however, until the late 1800's. There are three major centers today: Carlsbad, potash; Silver City area, copper, zinc, and lead; and Grants, uranium.

148

QUESTION: WHERE ARE THE OTHER OIL PUMPS AND TANKS IN THE SAN JUAN BASIN?

The potash mining east of Carlsbad, a $75 million-a-year industry employing more than 3600 persons, is the largest operation of its kind in the world. Six mining companies are active in the area, and a seventh is developing yet another mine. *Potash* is a word used to denote various potassium compounds. The principal ore mineral at Carlsbad is sylvanite, a mixture of potassium chloride and sodium chloride (common salt). The ore contains the equivalent of 21 to 25 per cent potassium oxide (K_2O).* Another ore mineral, known as *langbeinite*, a double salt of potassium and magnesium sulfate, is also mined.

The potash ores occur as horizontal beds sandwiched between thick salt and anhydrite layers. These beds are the result of evaporation of large quantities of salt waters during the latter part of the Permian period some 240 million years ago. The potash-bearing horizons now are buried from 900 to 1800 feet below the surface. The discovery of potash in southeast New Mexico was almost by accident. In 1925, the Snowden and Mc-Sweeny Company drilled a wildcat oil test a few miles east of Carlsbad. The hole was dry, but potash minerals were detected in the drill cuttings. The discovery generated considerable interest because the United States was forced to import most of its potash prior to this time. Further drilling proved the existence of tremendous deposits of potassium salts in that area.

The potash mines are among the most highly mechanized of the

* K_2O is the common unit used in pricing and assaying potassium salts. However, the potash is sold as purified potassium chloride or sulfate.

mineral industry. Access to the buried deposits is gained by vertical shafts. Actual mining is now done to a large extent by continuous miners, machines which bore or rip the potash ore from the face and load it into shuttle cars in one continuous operation. The shuttle cars then transport the ore to conveyor belts which move it to the shafts for hoisting. Working conditions and safety are excellent and have led to high productivity from these mines.

The potash ore is refined or processed by fractional crystallation or flotation. These plants remove most of the unwanted sodium chloride and other gangue minerals to produce high-quality potassium chloride or sulfate. After processing, the potash salts are stored in giant bins to await shipment by rail to the major agriculture areas of the United States. The Carlsbad mines produce some 15 million tons of ore a year which, when refined, produces 4 million tons of marketable potassium salts having a K_2O equivalent of 2.5 million tons.

Uranium mining is the newest major industry in New Mexico. The boom started in 1950 with the discovery of uranium ore west of Grants by a Navajo sheep rancher named Paddy Martinez. This discovery started one of the most extensive exploration and development campaigns in all mining history. By 1957, the area had proved uranium reserves accounting for more than half of the entire reserve of the nation. These discoveries will make this country self-sufficient in this vital atomic energy metal for

(Courtesy International Minerals & Chemical Corp.)

CRUNCH! . . . CONTINUOUS MINING MACHINE AT WORK

years to come. Five mills were built that are capable of producing "yellow cake" (almost pure uranium oxide) from uranium ores containing as little as 0.20 per cent U_3O_8. Four mills are located in the Grants area, ranging in capacity from 1500 to 4000 tons a day. The fifth mill, rated at 500 tons a day, is at Shiprock.

There are numerous mines, ranging from tiny two-man operations up to great mines producing more than 1000 tons a day. The most prolific producing area is the Ambrosia Lake District north of Grants; most of these mines are underground. Probably the largest single uranium mine, however, is the open-pit Jackpile–Paguate mine of the Anaconda Company on the Laguna Indian Reservation some thirty miles east of Grants. The mine uses electric shovels capable of loading eight cubic yards of ore at a time into large diesel trucks.

Copper is produced from the Chino mine located at Santa Rita, about fifteen miles east of Silver City. This mine, operated by Kennecott Copper Corporation, is the showpiece of the New Mexico minerals industry. The copper ore is low grade, containing only sixteen pounds a ton of the red metal, but the deposit is immense, allowing the mining of 22,500 tons a day. The Chino is by far the largest single mining operation in the state. A large concentrator and smelter are located at Hurley, about ten miles southwest of the pit.

The Chino pit is a spectacular sight for its scenic setting and its sheer size. The deposit is located below the Kneeling Nun, a famous natural statue formed by the erosion of a rhyolite flow which caps a high mesa. The pit covers almost one square mile and is 800 feet deep. The mining is highly mechanized. Large rotary drills make blast holes twelve inches in diameter into which explosives are loaded. A single blast may break 100,000 tons of rock. The ore is loaded with 8-cubic-yard shovels into large trucks carrying from 25 to 65 tons each. The trucks transport the ore to an inclined skipway on the west end of the pit. The skip then carries the ore up to the train level where it is transferred into railroad cars for shipment to the mill. Waste rock, too low-grade to justify sending to the mill, is transported to the very top of the skipway, where it is trucked to the dumps. At Chino, much of the waste rock contains some copper. The amount is small, but a part of it can be recovered by leaching—percolating water down through the rock to dissolve the copper. At the bottom of the dumps, the copper-rich water is collected and sent through precipitating tanks containing scrap iron. The copper plates out on the iron, forming metallic copper. The dump-leaching program alone at Chino is a substantial enterprise.

The concentrator and smelter at Hurley is the facility which reduces the low-grade ore into pure metal. The concentrator first crushes and grinds the ore, then recovers the copper-bearing minerals (principally chalcocite and chalcopyrite) by flotation. The concentrate of these copper sulfides is taken to the smelter to make metallic copper.

North and west of the Chino mine are important deposits of zinc and lead. Two underground mines are now active: the Hanover of the

152

New Jersey Zinc Company and the Kearney–Pewabic of American–Peru Mining Company. Although dwarfed by the Chino mine, these are important producers.

Copper, potash, and uranium are not the only mining operations of New Mexico. Perlite is recovered from deposits near No Agua in Taos County and just north of Grants. Two new gypsum plants are now operat-

(*Courtesy Kennecott Copper Corp.*)

"JUST SCOOP UP COPPER ORE, TAKE IT TO THE SKIPWAY . . ." UP THE SIDE OF THE CHINO MINE AT SANTA RITA

ing northeast of Albuquerque, and a cement plant is located east of that city. High-grade copper veins are worked south of Lordsburg. Coal mining is being reactivated, with producing mines near Gallup, Fruitland, and Raton. A new molybdenum mine is under development east of Questa. New Mexico's mineral industry is on a broad and firm base.

Mines and derricks are ever-present aspects of New Mexico's landscapes; they are seen by every citizen of the state and every tourist as he travels across the plains, valleys, and mountains. The derricks and the mine openings are merely surface features through which the vast wealth of the underground is exploited, but they are a monetarily important part of New Mexico's scenery, rocks, and history.

Enchanting Landscapes

by FRANK E. KOTTLOWSKI

The visitor and the native may be well acquainted with the more famous scenic places in New Mexico. Most of these are National or State Parks or Monuments—glistening dunes of White Sands, sandstone cliffs of El Morro, canyons eroded in volcanic rocks of Bandelier, the recent volcano of Capulin Mountain, multicolored sinkholes at Bottomless Lakes, grotesque carvings of volcanic rocks at City of Rocks, and the black tongues of cooled lava in the Valley of Fires State Park near Carrizozo.

Many of the lesser-known spectacular scenic areas are off the beaten path, far from the seventy-mile-an-hour Interstate highways. Even a brief description of all would fill a thick book. But near the most traveled routes are numerous enchanting landscapes. The traveler from the midwest or east, driving U.S. Highway 66 (Interstate 40) breaks over the edge of the "caprock" a few miles east of the New Mexico–Texas line. Atop the caprock is Llano Estacado, the Staked Plains, a level surface stretching along the southeast edge of New Mexico eastward into Texas. As seen south of Tucumcari near Ragland, east of Fort Sumner near Taiban, or east of Roswell near Kenna and Caprock, the bluffs of the Llano Estacado are topped by caprock, a cliff of white caliche-limestone as much as forty feet thick in places. Below, on gentle to steep slopes reaching northward toward Tucumcari or westward toward Fort Sumner and Roswell, are the varicolored red, purple, green, and gray shales and sandstones of Triassic age. Red Lake near Taiban on U.S. Highway 60-84 lies in the red muds of these Triassic rocks.

South of Tucumcari, rising boldly from the red-earth lowlands draining to the Canadian River, are Tucumcari Mountain and Mesa Redonda, and to the northwest the long buff cliffs of Mesa Rica. The latter mesa lies north of Interstate 40 as far west as Newkirk. Patches of the white caprock caliche-limestone cap these eastern New Mexico sentinels, whereas in other localities, the brown Dakota Sandstone tops the buttes and is underlain by pink Jurassic sandstones, with the mesa bases made up of the Triassic redbeds.

Near Santa Rosa, Interstate 40 dips down into the narrow green valley of Rio Pecos. Roadcuts lining the steep hills into the city show the red and brown sandstones and shales of the Triassic beds.

Driving westward from Santa Rosa, one crosses rolling hills near Clines Corners, then dips gently down into the northern part of the Estancia Basin near Moriarty. To the north on the horizon are the snow-capped peaks of the Sangre de Cristo Mountains. From Moriarty, Interstate 40 pulls slowly upward toward Edgewood into the eastern foothills of the Sandia Mountains, the grassy plains giving way to juniper and piñon groves.

From the downgrade into Tijeras Canyon, State Highway 10 leads north to San Antonito and the turnoff to Sandia Crest. The crest road winds up canyon walls, on sloping limestone mesas, up through thick stands of ponderosa pine, aspen, and, near the top, Engelmann spruce and corkbark fir. Rocky Mountain bighorn sheep may be seen off the road on the high crags. From Sandia Crest, 10,678 feet above sea level, much of north-central New Mexico is visible; Mount Taylor to the west, the Nacimiento and Jemez mountains to the northwest, the mighty Sangre de Cristo Mountains to the northeast, and countless ranges to the south and southwest. The city of Albuquerque is spread out at the base of the Sandias, and the twisting north-south channel of the Rio Grande stretches, glistening, as far left and right as one can see.

From Tijeras, Interstate 40 plunges into Tijeras Canyon, slicing through vertical roadcuts in Pennsylvanian limestones and shales, then through the ancient Precambrian granite. At the canyon's mouth, the road levels off on the broad alluvial plain on which much of east Albuquerque is built, although the "downtown" is really down, in the valley of the Rio Grande.

Westward, Interstate 40 rolls up out of the valley, crosses windswept plains spotted with black volcanic cones, in and out of the shallow brown valley of Rio Puerco, and then to the red-cliff-bordered valley of Rio San Jose. Cliffs are of brown, buff, and light-gray Jurassic sandstones, with the valley carved in Triassic redbeds. Near Laguna, on the north side of the valley, white gypsum of the Todilto Formation crops out. Then through the pink Jurassic cliffs the canyon winds, and near New Laguna, the highway is bordered by the varicolored, uranium-bearing Morrison beds, which are overlain by brown sandstones and black shales of Cretaceous age.

But as Interstate 40 approaches Grants, the dominant feature is black frozen lava. The mesas surrounding Mount Taylor are capped by black basalt, built up in many layers, each individual flows, and loose blocks tumble down on the hillsides. Young basalt, twisted and wrinkled as if it were still hot, winds along the valley; just east of Grants, a huge "field" of this recent basalt stretches southward beyond the horizon. And above all looms Mount Taylor, remnant of an ancient volcano, snow-capped in winter, towering 11,389 feet above sea level.

At Casa Blanca, southeast of Mount Taylor, State Road 23 leads south to Acoma Pueblo. Eleven miles to the southwest, Enchanted Mesa, *Katsim* as it is called by the Acomas, towers 450 feet above the surrounding valley floor. This sheer-cliffed rock is built by layers of (from the base to the top) pink and white Entrada Sandstone, gray Todilto limestone, pink and green Summerville beds, a massive cliff of light-tan Zuni Sandstone, and a cap of yellow-brown Dakota Sandstone.

The top of Enchanted Mesa is inaccessible by normal means. Legend has it that once the Acomas lived there, and there are Indian ruins up on the isolated rim. A terrific rain and lightning storm, one summer day, sent huge waterfalls down the sides of the mesa, tearing away large blocks of sandstone, and destroyed the trail to the top, a series of narrow zigzag

156

TALK ABOUT WIDE OPEN SPACES . . . AROUND THE ENCHANTED MESA

ledges and toeholds in crevasses. Thus the Acoma Indians moved a few miles to the southwest to Acoma, onto the top of another sheer cliff, a rock fortress carved in Zuni Sandstone and capped by Dakota Sandstone.

Southwest of Grants, the forested Zuni Mountains rise, bordered on the north by a valley cut in Triassic redbeds and on the east by the recent black basalt flows. The hurrying traveler will follow Interstate 40 to Gallup around the north edge of the Zuni dome, flanked on the north by the spectacular pink, red, brown, and gray cliffs of Jurassic and Cretaceous sandstones. If one has time, take the low road, State Highways 53 and 36, around the southern edge of the Zunis. For almost twenty miles, passing through San Rafael, the paved highway parallels the west edge of the Grants black basalt flow; then up over low ridges and past black cinder cones toward El Morro. In the lava tunnels, perpetual ice stays hidden from the sun; these can be visited at Ice Caves.

El Morro, Inscription Rock, with its towering cliffs of Zuni Sandstone, overlooks peaceful green valleys; farther west, the red and brown sandstones are carved into many mesas and buttes near Zuni Pueblo. Then northward to Gallup, swinging around the west edge of the Zuni Mountains, the roller-coaster highway, State 36, cuts through ponderosa pine country, bordered by Cretaceous brown sandstones, black shales, and coal beds.

Northeast of Gallup eight miles is Kit Carson's Cave, a gaping door on the face of a massive cliff of Jurassic sandstone. A pool of cool water lies along its floor. The three-and-a-half-mile drive north of Interstate 40

157

is through a vast broken country of sandstone spires, pyramids, cliffs, and ledges carved in the Jurassic rocks. Near Gallup, the drab coal-bearing Cretaceous beds form the landscapes, but westward near the Arizona line, erosion has cut down again to the brilliantly colored Jurassic rocks, and Interstate 40 is escorted westward into the Grand Canyon State by cliffs of white and pink sandstone.

Californians crossing New Mexico in the winter are likely to travel U.S. Highway 70-80 (Interstate 10) eastward. New Mexico is entered just before Steins Pass, which is channeled through the tan and green volcanic rocks of the Peloncillo Mountains. Then down across the mud and salt marshes of Alkali Flats lying in the Animas Valley and up onto the north edge of the Pyramid Mountains into Lordsburg. Mine dumps dot the Pyramids, and the ghost mining town of Shakespeare lies amid the purple volcanic rocks.

Eastward from Lordsburg for 118 miles are the Antelope Plains; plains, plains, plains. Steers graze on the sparse grass, yucca clumps border the highway, and here and there sand dunes flee before the restless winds. Mountain ranges, like islands on the sea of grass, yucca, and creosote bush, rise in the distance. West of Deming, the low Victorio Mountains lie south of the highway, made up of dolomite, limestone, and andesite ridges. Southeast of Deming are the lofty Florida Mountains, their northern toe crossed by Interstate 10. Volcanic hills dot the landscape east of Las Cruces, Sierra de las Uvas' purple slopes to the north, and the Potrillo Mountains and Mount Riley to the south. The latter are part of a spectacular volcanic field where black cinder cones and basalt flows cover hundreds of square miles, and craters such as Kilbourne Hole are sunk below the plains.

The descent into the Rio Grande Valley is awesome, especially if the late afternoon sun is dancing on the spires and cliffs of the Organ Mountains to the east. From across the brown plains, Interstate 10 winds down into the green Mesilla Valley, a different world of cotton and alfalfa fields, pecan and cottonwood groves, and red-tile-roofed Spanish homes. The view of the Organ Mountains alone is worth the trip.

At Las Cruces, a city booming on cotton, rockets, and tourists, Interstate 10 turns south to parallel the east side of the Rio Grande Valley down to Texas and El Paso. If one prefers a quiet scenic route, State Highway 28 winds its way along the west side of the Valley amid fields and groves, through peaceful villages, to end at the bridge over the Rio Grande on the edge of El Paso. Here, to the south, is El Cristo Rey, a cone of massive andesite, flanked by steeply tilted beds of limestone and shale, Early Cretaceous in age, cut in two by the New Mexico–Mexico border. Atop the peak is a 29-foot-high, 40-ton, limestone statue of Christ; a winding path leads upward from the base for those strong enough of limb to make the climb. Beyond, to the south, Ciudad Juarez lies, famous for its bordertown flavor, markets, cathedrals, and bull rings.

The traveler to the east should stay on U.S. 62-180 from El Paso. This highway cuts through the Hueco Mountains via Powwow Canyon, a gash carved from Pennsylvanian and Permian limestones, crosses the Diablo Plateau, rolls past the white patches of Salt Flat lakes, then winds up to the summit of Guadalupe Pass between the Delaware Mountains on the south and the towering Guadalupe Mountains on the north. Looking north from the Pass, Guadalupe Peak, highest point in Texas, and El Capitan are unforgettable sights, their steep lower slopes ribbed brown and green, overshadowed by the 1000-foot limestone cliffs of the peaks. The limestone-hewn Guadalupe Mountains parallel the highway in New Mexico and are pitted with many caves, with Carlsbad Caverns the largest known in the range. Eastward beyond the Pecos Valley stretches the Great Plains and Texas.

A side trip, near Carlsbad, over black-topped and gravel roads leads from Seven Rivers, up Rocky Arroyo on State Road 137, into the northern foothills of the Guadalupe Mountains to Sitting Bull Falls. Here, cool spring waters cascade over limestone ledges to join in green pools lying amid the cottonwood groves of the canyon floor.

Lake McMillan, a reservoir along the Pecos River north of Carlsbad, and the many potash mines east of Carlsbad are parts of the enchanting landscapes of this southeastern corner. Northward, following the green cotton fields bordering the Pecos River, U.S. Highway 285 leads through Artesia with its oil refineries to modern booming Roswell, second city of the state. East of Roswell, bordering the east side of the Pecos Valley, is Bottomless Lakes, azure blue pools spotted in sink holes.

Eastward from Roswell, on either U.S. Highway 70 or 380, redbeds of Permian and Triassic age lie half hidden by pinkish sands up to the edge of the caprock; beyond are the fertile grazing and crop lands of the Llano Estacado, with its queen cities of Clovis and Portales. Here, deep wells pump underground waters to irrigate lush fields that produce peanuts, tomatoes, sweet potatoes, melons, strawberries, cucumbers, and grapes. On the plains beyond the reach of the wells, wheat, maize, and broomcorn are grown. Southeastward, oil derricks dot the plains, surrounding Hobbs and Lovington.

Westward from Roswell, U.S. Highways 70 and 380 run together up the rolling limestone hills west of the Pecos Valley before plunging down Picacho Hill into the narrow canyon of Rio Hondo. At Hondo they divide. U.S. Highway 380 leads northwestward through Lincoln town, Billy the Kid's shooting grounds, into Capitan, over Indian Divide, and down into sleepy Carrizozo—paralleled by the forested peaks of Capitan Mountains to the north and overshadowed by mighty Sierra Blanca to the southwest. U.S. Highway 70 runs up the green canyon of Rio Ruidoso, past Ruidoso Downs, past State Highway 37 which leads to Ruidoso and the Sierra Blanca Ski Area, up into the ponderosa pines, crossing the divide at Apache Summit, then westward and downhill past Mescalero, paralleling Rio Tularosa. Suddenly the canyon widens, and ahead is the dry Tularosa Basin with the White Sands glistening in the far distance.

From Tularosa to Alamogordo, U.S. Highway 70 is along the west edge of the Sacramento Mountains wherein tier upon tier of dolomite

(Forest Service, U.S.D.A.)
NOW THIS IS WHAT IS MEANT BY FOREST . . . FROM MONJEAU LOOKOUT

and limestone cliffs rise to the high peaks near Cloudcroft. Southwestward from Alamogordo, the highway cuts diagonally across the Tularosa Basin, skirting the southern edge of the White Sands, and passing through White Sands Missile Range. Ahead lie the fabulous spires of the Organ Mountains; to the right, the notched cliffs of the San Andres Mountains stretch northward to rounded Salinas Peak and beyond the horizon. Steeply, the highway rises to cross San Augustin Pass between the Organ and San Andres mountains, past the village of Organ with its crumbling mining dumps, before plunging downward onto the southern end of Jornada del

Muerto, and finally, on the east edge of Las Cruces, leaves the creosote bush plains to dip into the green Mesilla Valley of the Rio Grande.

West of Carrizozo, U.S. 380 crosses the black basalt flows of Valley of Fires State Park, curves over the Carrizozo dome and up the dip slopes of Chupadera Mesa, crosses in red roadcuts the northern tip of Sierra Oscura, then westward through sand dunes of the northern Jornada del Muerto. Coal beds crop out at Cerro Colorado before the highway sweeps down into the Rio Grande Valley to San Antonio.

U.S. Highway 60 enters the state from the east on the Staked Plains near booming Clovis, crosses Rio Pecos Valley at Fort Sumner—near Billy the Kid's grave—goes straight as a beeline over the plains to Vaughn, then crosses the low southern end of the Pedernal Hills where tan Permian sandstones lie abruptly on Precambrian granite, quartzite, and schists. Near Willard, the highway crosses the southern end of the Estancia Valley, with the salt lakes of Laguna del Perro mere remnants of the huge Pleistocene lake that once filled the Valley. West from Mountainair, Abo redbeds border the highway; limestone walls of Gran Quivira lie to the south and the red sandstone church ruins of Abo and Quarai are to the north. Through Abo Pass between the Manzano and Los Pinos mountains the highway runs, then down the long alluvial fan slopes to the Rio Grande Valley at Bernardo. From Bernardo to Socorro, U.S. Highway 60 joins Interstate 25; westward from Socorro, the road climbs out of the Valley onto Snake Ranch Flats, parallels the snow-tipped Magdalena Mountains to Magdalena, then crosses the north end of the grassy San Agustin Plains. Westward to Datil and Quemado, the highway is always in sight of volcanic mountains, up and down winding canyons, and across intermontane plains.

Still westward into Arizona along U.S. Highway 60 are Springerville, fabulous Salt River Canyon, the mining cities of Globe, Miami, and Superior, and booming Phoenix.

Into this west-central New Mexico country of volcanic peaks and grassy plains comes U.S. Highway 180 from Deming northwestward. Along the scenic, winding route are City of Rocks, the copper smelter at Hurley, Santa Rita's huge open-pit copper mine, famous Silver City, colorful canyons of the Gila and San Francisco rivers, and, crossed by passes or bordering all routes, the rugged rhyolite, andesite, and basalt ledges and cliffs.

From El Paso to Raton Pass, 515 miles, U.S. Highway 85 (Interstate 25) crosses New Mexico from south to north, from Mexico to Colorado. As far as La Bajada Hill, between Albuquerque and Santa Fe, the highway parallels the Rio Grande. Northward from El Paso, past Las Cruces to Radium Springs and old Fort Selden, the green Mesilla Valley borders the route; then through Selden Canyon into the Hatch Valley near San Diego Mountain, and along the west side of the bold cliffs of the Caballo Mountains, past Caballo Reservoir to Truth or Consequences (old Hot Springs). Eastward lies Elephant Butte Dam and reservoir; the road cuts across alluvial plains to the west of the Rio Grande all the way to Albuquerque, with the mountains to the west the San Mateo, Magdalena,

Socorro, and Ladron and to the east, the Fra Cristobal, Los Pinos, and Manzano.

Intersecting Interstate 40 at Albuquerque, the Pan-American Central Highway, Interstate 25 crosses to the east side of the Rio Grande, the sheer cliffs of the Sandia Mountains to the east and the distant dark green Jemez Mountains to the northwest. Crossing Galisteo Creek northeast of Santo Domingo Pueblo, Interstate 25 turns toward the northeast, climbs La Bajada Hill, onto the green plains sloping from Santa Fe. Santa Fe, the ancient capital city, is nestled on the edge of the Sangre de Cristo Mountains. Southeastward and eastward, U.S. Highway 85 (to be Interstate 25 here) rolls, skirting the southern end of the Sangre de Cristo Mountains, wedged in by the north-facing cliffs of Glorieta Mesa, through Glorieta Pass, where the Confederates lost the battle for the Southwest, across the upper reaches of Rio Pecos, and around to Las Vegas. Then in straight lines across the western edges of the Great Plains where they lap up onto the Sangre de Cristo ranges, through Wagon Mound and Springer to Raton. The climb up-canyon to Raton Pass, through roadcuts of brown sandstone, shale, and coal, leads into Colorado, with a view of much of southern Colorado from the Pass.

Many routes lead northward from ancient Santa Fe. U.S. Highway 285 crosses the high divide near Bishop's Lodge, follows Rio Tesuque to Pojoaque, crosses the Rio Grande near Espanola amid varicolored badlands cut in the Santa Fe rocks, then heads northward on the black basalt plateau toward Colorado. Black Mesa, a volcanic neck, lies south of Espanola, overlooking the green Rio Grande Valley; atop this height, Pueblo Indians once defied Spanish guns until they starved. Northward, near Tres Piedras, the Ortega and Brazos ranges tower to the west, the perlite-rich hills of No Agua lie to the northeast, and across the basalt plains cut by the Rio Grande, the lofty, snow-capped Sangre de Cristo Mountains loom.

At Pojoaque, State Road 4 leads westward, across Otowi bridge of the Rio Grande, then winds up into the canyon and mesa country bordering the Jemez Mountains. Herein lie Bandelier and Los Alamos, one with ancient abandoned pueblos, the other the atomic city. Farther west, the road crosses the rim of an ancient volcano into Valle Grande, the crater of that volcano—some 16 miles across. When this volcano spewed forth hot ashes about a million years ago, the volcanic dust was wind-blown as far as Kansas and Nebraska!

At Espanola, U.S. Highway 84 breaks away to the northwest to follow Rio Chama in its canyon carved from redbeds near Abiquiu, past the interesting museum at Ghost Ranch—where bones of Triassic dinosaurs are collected—Echo Amphitheater, El Vado Lake, through Chama, and on up into the San Juan Mountains country of southern Colorado.

Near Espanola, U.S. Highway 64 splits off to the northeast; this is the high road of north-central New Mexico. Paralleling the canyon of the Rio Grande to Pilar, the highway climbs up onto the Taos plateau to Taos, turns eastward to cut through the Sangre de Cristo Mountains over Palo Flechado Pass, down into the grassy Moreno Valley to Eagle Nest and Eagle Nest Lake, then eastward again following the narrow canyon of the Cimarron River to Cimarron and Raton. A loop trip northward from Eagle Nest on State 38 goes through ghost town Elizabethtown, over Red River Pass, and down the varicolored canyon of Red River to Questa, before turning southward toward Taos.

And there is the northwest, the Four Corners region, land of Navajos and gas wells, presided over by magnificent Shiprock. State Highway 44 leaves Interstate 25 at Bernalillo, follows Rio Salado to San Ysidro, which nestles at the south tip of the Nacimiento Mountains below White Mesa, thence northwestward past Cabezon Peak and coaly La Ventana to Cuba in the valley of Rio Puerco. Then, up and down, the winding highway cuts transversely across the San Juan Basin, through pine groves at the Continental Divide, past the side road to Chaco Canyon National Monument at Blanco Trading Post, and among the multicolored Tertiary beds carved into badlands. At Bloomfield, oil and gas wells lie all about, and the mesa-and-canyon country gives way to the valley of the San Juan River. At Aztec, State Road 44 joins U.S. Highway 550 in the narrow valley of the Animas River—a clear cold stream sent rushing down from the icy lakes of the San Juan Mountains to the north. Eastward a few miles lies Navajo Lake along the San Juan River; northward, U.S. 550

(*U.S. Park Service*)
SUBDIVISION LIVING, PUEBLO STYLE—AT AZTEC NATIONAL MONUMENT

163

winds up the Animas Valley toward Durango, high Silverton, and Mesa Verde National Park. Aztec Ruins National Monument is just to the northwest of Aztec.

Westward from Aztec, U.S. Highway 550 follows the Animas River to its junction with the San Juan River, then past the huge Navajo coal mine, a long open cut near Fruitland, to junction with U.S. Highway 666 at Shiprock.

Shiprock! A buttressed needle, towering 1450 vertical feet above Navajo-land, with walls of black igneous rock radiating from its feet like spokes on a wheel. This dark-colored spire once filled the throat of a volcano. Where are piles of rocks, hundreds of feet thick, that once surrounded it? Down the river they went, down the San Juan to the Colorado River, and thence to the ocean.

To the west, as a background, are the forested Carrizo, Lukachukai, and Chuska mountains. Off to the east lies Hogback Mountain, an up-turned ridge of sedimentary rocks producing oil—the petroleum geologist's favorite haunt, an anticline.

Southward from Shiprock, U.S. 666 passes other volcanic necks such as Bennett Peak and Ford Butte. North of Gallup, State Road 68 leads westward to Window Rock (Arizona), the Indian Headquarters of the Navajo Reservation. Near Gallup, coal beds of Late Cretaceous age crop out, Gamerco once being a booming coal-mining town. Now huge drag-line shovels scoop out the coal from open pits to the northwest of Gallup. And at Gallup, the Indian Capital, a loop drive around the San Juan Basin is completed; Interstate 40, old U.S. Highway 66, goes eastward to Albuquerque, St. Louis, and Chicago, and westward to Grand Canyon, Los Angeles, and the blue Pacific.

Many other scenic places dot the Land of Enchantment; local hosts, rancher or city dweller, know of these. Mountain meadows, rushing streams, rocky peaks, desert valleys, badlands, grassy plains, thick forests, spectacular chasms, needle rocks, and brilliant colors—they are all here in New Mexico.

Composition:	Linotype Fairfield
	Text—10/11
	Index—8/9 (reduced to 6/7)
	Display heads—18 pt. Bulmer italic
Presswork:	38″ Miehle Single Color Offset
	29″ Harris Single Color Offset
Binding:	Smyth sewn and glued
Paper:	Text—70# white matte
	Cover—12 pt. Kivar

Index